Almost an
Englishman

Almost an Englishman

Charles Hannam

ANDRE DEUTSCH

First published in 1979 by
André Deutsch Limited
105 Great Russell Street London WC1

Printed in Great Britain by
Bristol Typesetting Company Limited
Barton Manor – St Philips
Bristol

British Library Cataloguing in Publication Data

Hannam, Charles
  Almost an Englishman.
  1. Great Britain – Social life and customs –
  20th century
  I. Title
  942.084'092'4   DA566.4

  ISBN 0-233-97119-x

First published in the
United States of America 1979

Library of Congress No. 78-74471

For Pam

Almost an
Englishman

Introduction

In my first book, *A Boy in your Situation,* I explored my childhood. It was all so far removed from the person I am now that I could not use the personal pronoun and I began to write about myself as 'Karl' in the third person. I was looking at a boy who by the end of the book had just moved into adolescence. In some ways it was easier to write about early childhood: there were powerful adults, sorrow and pain, and Karl defended himself against all these forces by living a secret life where he could act out his fantasies by stealing, lying, eating vast quantities of food, and inventing magic rituals against the hostile world of Nazi Germany. He had a secret word and when he used it he imagined it would destroy all the things he hated: his teachers, the school and the members of the Hitler Youth in his class. Karl was a victim and the persecutors were enemies that were clearly identifiable. When I came to write this book, *Almost an Englishman,* new problems had to be faced. I had to look at the move from adolescence to young adulthood – not an easy time to explore. Most of us find this part of our lives so gruesome that not only do we try to forget it the best we can but we are deeply upset when our children or pupils become adolescent. It is not easy to separate out what is envy and what is an embarrassed forgetfulness; certainly the gangling, sulking and critical youth that I became does not seem to me to be very likeable. Karl was no longer fat; wartime rationing and boarding school diet had seen to that. But the problems of his inner life remained. How could he come to terms with the two sorts of society in which he moved? One was the new school which

A*
9

accepted him unquestioningly and made him want desperately to be an Englishman and the other was the world of Jewish refugees, his own people, but from whom he felt increasingly alienated. Since the beginning of the Nazi persecution Karl had learnt to hate the Jewish part of himself. In the first place the religion did not mean much to him as his family had not been religious beyond the needs of conformity and respectability. Karl himself had deep doubts about the existence of a god, and the religious education he had duly received had not kindled in him either pride in his Jewish heritage or an understanding of the history and fate of the Jews. Then, in some way, the hatred the Nazis had directed at Jews had become part of Karl's inner feelings about himself. Why after all had he been thrown out of the country where his family had been settled for many generations unless he or other Jews had done something to deserve their fate? He had come to believe that if only he had not been a Jew all would have been well, and what seemed to him so unfair was that he, after all, was not one of those 'typical' Jews the Nazis caricatured in their party papers. Was his hair not fair and straight, his eyes blue and his nose uncrooked? So his sense of self-hate and injustice was turned against other Jews. To add to this feeling what remained of the Jewish community, his own family, those who paid his school fees and those who put him up during the holidays were all refugees. Among them he felt a stranger. He detested their bad English; their mixture of German, Yiddish and English words seemed to him alien. They talked with their hands and they wore continental clothes. Karl wanted to be like his teachers and friends at school whom he admired, whose manners and attitudes he was learning to respect and adopt; most of all he wanted to be accepted, and if the price was the rejection of the people to whom he had once belonged, it seemed well worth paying at that time. Here was a deep conflict, because however critical of his own, Jewish, people Karl was, he was also amused and moved by their humour and their stories. He loved the food they ate, although he never failed to be critical of the way they obtained it, and he loved the authority he had with them because he knew so much more than they about the ways of the new country. The conflict could not be resolved and Karl became very hostile and over-critical of the very people who sustained him. This is the problem of every adolescent; somehow in order to assert himself he must rebel against the authority on which he is also dependent. This is not a time for either tolerance or gratitude, and mostly adolescents in their own families find it necessary to behave badly and ungraciously in order to be able to say 'I am not a child any more and what I want I need to receive as a right, not as a favour.' The refugee is in a worse position because he cannot demand natural things as a right. Karl's mother was dead and he had no idea what had become of his father in Germany; only his sister, who was older than he, remained. Karl was always a guest, not quite a member of the family, and if he were to behave badly there was the threat that he might have to go back to the approved school he had lived in for a few months as a refugee, and where it seemed to him he had spent all his time doing nothing but turn the handle of the potato-sorting machine. He had the critical clarity of all adolescents, only his had to be even sharper because his very survival depended on it. He had to observe and judge the moods of those on whom he depended, and that meant there was little room for generosity or detachment in him. He could not admit to himself that the refugees he so much rejected were themselves struggling to make a new life. Their ingenuity and resilience seemed repulsive to Karl and when they were generous to him, and they often were, he accepted the generosity without a sense of gratitude. He could not afford to be beholden to anyone because that would have meant he could not be a person in his own right. What Karl wanted most was security, love and affection but when he was shown any he could not accept it without suspicion or resentment. When Karl joined the army, the civilized values he had absorbed at his school were again threatened. None of the values he had encountered at Elmfield existed there; there was brutality and bullying. Worse, when he was sent to India and witnessed the end of the British Empire, he saw a rotten institution which did little for the people for whose benefit it was meant to exist. Both the officers and the men he lived with had attitudes towards the Indians, their civilization and their customs that contained

11

the same mixture of contempt, hate and ignorance that the Nazis had shown towards the Jews.

And yet I found happiness in the army. I had mates: 'they may not have been very choice, but they were my mates', and they accepted and tolerated me with a generosity which I still find moving. For the first time in my life it seemed to me that I belonged somewhere.

I had decided to become an Englishman and so I failed to appreciate the qualities of the refugees I met, their courage, their resilience and their very special humour. On the other hand the English did not meet my needs either: they seemed to regret my foreignness and lack of 'class'. Only many years later was it possible to accept *all* aspects of my personality, the Jewish, the refugee and the English part. It took much time before I could say 'look, I am what I am, not what you want me to be'. Not only did it take a lot of time but I find that having looked at the young man I then was I have become mellower and even capable of gratitude!

CHARLES HANNAM
Bristol 1978

Chapter 1

'Quiet please.'

Steve banged a teaspoon against a cup. The boys stopped eating their thin pieces of bread, marge and jam. They stopped talking and they looked up. He was the headmaster.

'I just want to announce that I am appointing Karl Hartland as house-prefect. He has only been here a short time but he has earned our respect and I am sure you will be happy to co-operate with him.'

There was clapping, not thunderous clapping, as there had been for Harry Pring, who played for the school in nearly all games; just polite clapping. After tea the smaller boys crowded round Karl.

'Good, now that you are a prefect you can give us lines. Go on, give *him* fifty lines. Just say, "Take fifty lines for giving buck," and then he's got to do it. Aren't you going to give us lines? Go on.'

Karl felt he was blushing, but he wanted to seem cool and nonchalant so he just ignored the boys. Then Douglas came up to him. Douglas, the head of house, flat-faced, with thick glasses.

'Congratulations. Well, you are joining a select band. You can start by taking the fourth form for prep tonight and then you can come up to the study for toast; and just remember, don't let the little sods give you any buck, stamp on them straight away and you'll have no trouble. If there is any trouble, I'll sort them out.'

Karl thought, 'Oh god, not the fourth form; that's Axford, I can't do anything with him and they will all make trouble.'

He had desperately wanted to be a prefect. It was the brown

cap with the long peak. Ben had already suggested that he might be a prefect soon. 'You are quite tough but you aren't one of the games idiots and Steve is trying to have more intelligent prefects. You are older than the rest of us and now you are in the sixth; yes, he'll make you a prefect because he wants us refugees to have the same sort of chance as the others. You have only been here a short time and I bet he is quite impressed at how quickly you have learnt English. I mean, one day you turn up with a couple of suitcases and hardly a word of English, and a few months later you have got your school certificate and are starting in the sixth. Of course he'll make you a prefect.'

Ben had come from Vienna. He was younger than Karl, but he had been at the school longer and had taken Karl under his wing when he first came in 1940. He irritated Karl because he knew everything and was obviously much disliked by other boys and by the staff.

'They don't like me,' Ben had said, 'because they think I spy for Steve. The old guard hate us refugee boys – because we are too clever for them, and they can't understand that we hate the Germans as much as they do; they can't stand our being no good at games, either. Anyhow, I'm writing a paper on mastur-bation, treating the problem from the Freudian point of view. That's never been done before and perhaps I can present it at a psycho-analytical congress. They're held in London now.'

Karl never knew what Ben was really doing or what he might be up to. One thing was certain, Ben understood the school and had helped Karl a lot. If only he wouldn't sniff so often and put on that special, clever grin when he knew that no one else understood what he was talking about; that grated; and even if he was right most of the time, Karl still did not want him to be thought of as his only friend.

'*Your* friend Ben will look after you,' they had said. And now Karl was a prefect and had to look after the fourth form during prep, sitting on the teacher's platform. Prep came just after tea and everyone was supposed to be working. Karl saw Axford leaning across and whispering, then he bent over his own book, then he turned to his neighbour; then there was another whisper. He went on like that for some time.

14

'Axford, stop cribbing.'

'I'm not cribbing.'

'Oh, yes you are, I saw you; you were leaning over and I saw you cribbing.'

Axford ignored Karl. He leant over his neighbour's desk again and went on copying.

'Axford, if you go on copying I will give you fifty lines.'

'You and whose army? You can't give me lines. Learn to speak English properly before you give me orders.' He mimicked Karl: 'I vill gif you fifty lines.'

He rounded off the imitation by putting two fingers under his nose to look like a bristly moustache and giving a Hitler salute. Other boys were turning round and laughing and Karl felt his face going beetroot red. He realized that he had got 'v' and 'w' mixed up again, although it happened less often now than it used to and he was ever so careful. He wanted to say to Axford, 'Look, I have been talking English for only eight months – of course I make mistakes. You would make mistakes if you had to talk German, you stupid sod.'

Karl hated Axford, who had a thin, pinched face. The end of his nose was red and his eyes looked disgusting, there was pus on the eyelashes. And his tie: he couldn't even tie it properly. It was in a tight little knot, obviously he never undid it, and now it was greasy as well. And his voice squeaked.

'It's not fair.'

Karl knew it wasn't fair. In the first place he was not all that sure that Axford had really been cribbing.

'I was only borrowing a rubber; there's no law against that, is there? It's a free country, isn't it?'

'Christ,' thought Karl, 'first he makes cracks about my English and now he is calling me a fascist dictator. I will never be able to keep order after this. They will follow me round the yard hissing.' The boys had done that once to an unpopular prefect. Karl felt sure that Steve would ask him to hand in his gorgeous cap, he would be demoted – like Dreyfus – marched round the square and his cap would be taken off him.

Then he remembered Douglas. 'Don't let them give you any buck,' he had said.

'Fifty lines: "I must not copy my homework", and if you refuse I'll take you to the Head.'

'You wouldn't take me to Steve, you haven't got the nerve. Anyhow, you can't now, he's having his tea. Anyhow, you can't give lines, you are only a new prefect, it's not fair.'

Karl half hoped that Axford would refuse to get up. 'I'll slug him, I'll get him on the nose, then he will really have something to moan about,' he thought.

The last time Karl had hit another boy was in the approved school for boys. He had been dumped there when the refugee hostel he was living in closed down, soon after he had come to England from Essen. He was supposed to have trained as an agricultural worker there, but had hated the place and, one day, standing by the potato-sorting machine he had hit a boy. He remembered how his hand had hurt. In films when people hit each other one falls to the ground, but the hitter never feels the agony that Karl had felt. 'I'll get him on the nose,' Karl promised himself. But Axford got up.

There was a shocked silence; everyone was watching. Karl wanted to say, 'Let's call it off. Look, let's pretend we have seen the head, just apologise and the whole incident will be over.' But Axford looked sulky, and the anger rose in Karl again. He felt like taking him by the scruff of the neck, marching him along and then throwing him at Steve's feet, saying, 'He has been defying me, making jokes about my foreign accent; and he as much as said I am a fascist dictator and that's not fair when you consider that I am a refugee.'

They reached the door of the drawing room and when they went in Karl saw Steve standing by the fire with a cup of tea in his hand. It was a huge wood fire and the drawing room was painted all white. There were modern paintings on the walls. The furniture was made of oak.

'Very modern,' Ben had told Karl, 'you see they have superb taste and they couldn't find furniture to suit them so they had it specially made. She is frightfully rich, you know, and of course they both get paid and so they are very well off. Have you noticed the Dufy drawing? Superb.'

'Well, Karl, what is it?'

Steve looked a bit irritated. He was much taller than Karl. His hair was nearly white, receding on both sides of the forehead and his nose was very crooked. Karl had wondered if he was Jewish. He often wondered if people were Jewish. He had learnt how to tell from his family in Germany. You looked at noses, the colour of hair, any clue; with Steve Karl just did not know. Why was he so decent to the refugee boys? Why had he taken him from the camp without even finding out if he could cope with the work? Karl was also afraid of Steve. He had sudden outbursts of anger, great furious anger. Once Karl had forgotten to pass him a message and he had stormed into the classroom shouting, 'Hartland, you great fool, you fool with jingling bells on,' and afterwards another boy, Paul, had imitated Steve: 'Hartland, you fool'. Ben had said, 'You are afraid of him because he reminds you of your father, you are making a father-figure out of him and you have transferred your oedipal feelings to him.'

Ben was always on about Freud. It was partly because he, too, came from Vienna, although Ben had insisted, 'We are not Jewish, you know. My family was Greek Orthodox.'

'Greek Orthodox, my arse,' Karl replied. 'You only did that because you wanted to assimilate. With your nose and black hair, of course you are Jewish. Or else why on earth did they kick you out?'

Karl was hard on Ben but he needed him desperately. Ben knew, Ben understood, and Ben interpreted.

'Well, Karl, what is it?' Steve's voice broke into Karl's thoughts.

'I have brought Axford to see you, sir.' Karl nearly said 'Steve'. They called him Steve in the history lessons but he felt that this special occasion demanded a special approach.

'I gave him fifty lines and he said I could not give lines because I was a new prefect; he also said something about my accent.'

'Why on earth didn't you take him to the master on duty?'

Karl had not thought of that. Of course he should have gone to the master on duty. That was the correct procedure, and now he was a prefect he should know what to do, not rely on

Steve. He felt his knees go all soft and his face red. 'Steve will never think that I am a leader, a controller of unruly classes,' he thought. He had become excited and he had made the wrong decision. Just the sort of thing that might lose the war. A few weeks before he had had a row with 'Toss', the biology master, because he had refused to take a message to the matron. Toss had said, 'If you don't obey orders you won't be able to give orders. This is wartime, Karl. You have just refused to do what I told you. You have defied my authority.'

'I'm awfully sorry, sir, but I'm working,' Karl had replied. Toss had become furious, and Karl was terrified that he would be reported to Steve. But nothing happened, and now Karl himself was reporting Axford for disobedience. But defying an order was exciting. Karl suddenly thought of a time at home in Essen when he had called his poor old grandfather a dog's pisshole and refused to run an errand for him. His act of defiance had elated him.

'Only connect' Vanessa had said last week. She was Steve's wife, and the boys saw her every week to discuss their English essays and talk about the books they had been reading. 'Only connect'. She had made that remark in a discussion about E. M. Forster, but it was just as true of his life. Karl desperately wanted to 'connect'; he saw how close things he had done were to Axford's behaviour now, and he wanted to call the whole thing off. But there was Steve, looking cross, and Axford looking as if he was about to start snivelling again. He would have to go through with it.

'He was copying the prep from his neighbour, sir,' Karl said. 'I told him to stop, and he went on, so I gave him fifty lines.'

'Please, sir, I was only asking for a pencil, I wasn't cribbing.'

'Last time it was a rubber,' Karl came in sharply. 'At least be consistent.'

Steve looked irritated, more so now. He obviously thought it was absurd of Karl to bother him with this trivial matter. He put the cup of tea onto the mantelpiece.

'Him and his tea,' Karl thought, 'I bet that's why he's cross. I have interrupted the sacred tea ceremony and he won't back me up.'

18

But Steve turned to Axford. 'You know, you are only having Hartland on because he is new, and I won't have it. If he gives you lines you jolly well do them. Now go back and get on with your homework.'

Axford walked away looking pink and cross and then Steve turned to Karl. 'We really must have a talk about the nature of authority and punishment, Karl. Come and see me after you have finished your prep duty.'

When Karl came back Steve offered him a chair in his little study. There was a Braque reproduction on the wall and the shelves were full of art books. Steve lit his pipe. It went out again and again and he held a match over the bowl but nothing very much happened. Occasionally there would be a puff of smoke. Karl liked the smell. Now that he was a prefect he was allowed to smoke in the study, so he had already made up his mind to buy a pipe. He had seen one with a small fault that was only half-a-crown, and he had some pocket money saved. He felt a bit guilty about spending it on such a luxury, though. Before he had started at Elmfield his sister had warned him, 'Now, remember, the other Hartlands are paying for you. They are under no obligation to pay and you must be careful not to spend a penny more than you have to.'

Karl had taken the warning to heart. Anything was better than having to go back to the approved school. He had hated it there and remembered with particular horror the potato-sorting machine. For several weeks he had done nothing but turn the handle while the potatoes shuffled about inside and then fell out into three groups; small (pig potatoes), medium and large. He knew that this school was his only chance to do something with his life other than turn a handle on a machine. But the pipe was important to him. A man with a pipe in his hand seemed manly and full of authority. All Englishmen smoked pipes – Karl had already known that when he was still in Germany. Now he was determined to become an Englishman, and that obviously included being able to be a leader of men. Succeeding as a prefect was surely the first step towards it and it seemed to him that so far he had failed miserably. Even though Axford had been told to do the lines, he had still made a fool of

19

him and had teased him about his English. Now they would all laugh at him.

Between sucking at his pipe Steve began, 'It must be very difficult for you. You have come from an authoritarian environment, and here we try to create one where people co-operate rather than just obey. Do you know, Karl, I have been teaching for over twenty years now and I am beginning to realize that punishment does not work. My predecessor believed in caning boys, but I am trying to do without corporal punishment. Caning works in a limited sort of way – you get an immediate result, but not a long term relationship.'

Karl was angry about Steve's, 'you have come from an authoritarian environment.' Everyone seemed to think that at home in Germany they had all stood to attention shouting, 'Jawohl' – admittedly he used to click his heels but he had stopped doing that a long time ago. He was just as fed up with Steve's lack of understanding as with Axford's mockery. He wanted to say, 'All right, in that case why do you put a prefect in charge of prep and in particular a new prefect. How am I to cope with the Axfords of this world. Where I came from, at the approved school farm camp, you just slugged a boy and he soon did what he was told.'

Karl had conveniently forgotten how much he had hated being told what to do, and how frightened he had felt of getting into fights. What he remembered was that if you were going to fight you must attack, strike before you were struck. Unfortunately with that tick, Axford, it had not gone too well.

Steve looked at Karl and started on another tack. 'What is it like to be a Jew?' he asked. 'Do you know I am fascinated by the Jewish religion, the sense of uniqueness and the tremendous achievements of the race.' Karl's first thought was to say, 'I am not fascinated by the religion at all. It is meaningless to me. It destroyed our family.' But he suspected Steve would be disappointed. So he concentrated on the 'race' question.

'I very much doubt if there is such a thing as a Jewish race. I have thought about it a lot. The Germans claimed that they had discovered Jewish racial characteristics, but look at me; I don't conform to the standard type. Do you know, at school once I was made to stand in front of the class and the teacher used me to show the "typical" Aryan head shape.'

Steve roared with laughter. 'I must obviously think again about the concept of race. But I suppose what I am really talking about is the closed community, the way Jews exist apart from other communities and close themselves off from contact with others. In the end they and the outside community imagine that they have been chosen in some particular way. In the same way a class may "close itself" against the teacher or the prefect. By punishing or persecuting them you reinforce the prejudices they have about the outsider, and they become more cut off from you than before.'

Karl did not follow Steve's argument, but he felt pleased that the headmaster was talking to him, sitting opposite him in an armchair. He was grateful that his failure to control Axford was not being held against him, except in the form of an oblique discussion on the nature of groups and punishment. He felt intrigued that Steve was interested in his Jewishness and that his curiosity was kindly, almost scientific, and not intrusive. And yet he resented it. More than anything he wanted to become an Englishman, to disappear for ever into a new identity, a new language, and clothes that in no way distinguished him from other boys. When he had come to the school first his clothes from Germany had set him apart.

'Look at the coat Hartland is wearing,' the stupid geography master had shouted, 'it's tweed, and tweed comes from . . .' and he droned on, and the boys looked at Karl and he blushed and wished from the bottom of his heart that he had a grey flannel suit like the rest of them. If only the head would talk to him about something other than the exclusive nature of the Jewish race.

Karl explained to Steve, 'You see, we were German Jews and our family had been living in Essen for generations. We were "liberal"; that meant we did not keep the dietary laws strictly; we went to synagogue but I don't think it meant very much to any of us.'

'Do you mean,' Steve asked, 'you would have joined cause with the Germans if they had not persecuted your family?'

Karl was really embarrassed now; he didn't want to be disloyal to his family, but he needed to think this one through, and give Steve an honest answer.

'You see, my uncle fought in the First War, another uncle died in it and another was decorated. I think the family saw themselves as Germans rather than Jews, although they went to the synagogue and I was introduced into the religion by a special ceremony.' Karl did not think that Steve would understand if he said 'barmitzwah'. He was always careful with non-Jews not to bring in Jewish terms.

'You mean the barmitzwah,' Steve said.

Karl was surprised that he knew the word, after all he was a goy – no, goy was not the right word. That meant an insensitive, ignorant Christian and Steve was neither of those things; he had taken on at least fourteen refugees from Germany and Austria and had admitted Karl without question. When his sister, Margot, had gone to see Steve all she had said was, 'Please, can you take my brother into your school? He is very unhappy in a farm camp at the moment and he ought to be at school; he is only fourteen.' And Steve had taken him just like that. Karl was not sure why he had done it; he was not a Jew as far as he knew. And he talked to Karl in a way no grown-up had ever done before, a way which helped him to sort out his own ideas.

'I think the Nazis made us realize we were Jewish more than the Rabbi had done. I can't say I felt any great enthusiasm for the religion. I went through the ceremony but it meant no more than presents and a nice dinner. And I hated being Jewish at school. All the other boys did interesting things, like military exercises, and I was excluded. So I suspect that if Hitler had been decent to our family we would have been sympathetic to his nationalism, though I wish I could say with conviction that we would have opposed him and his lot. Mind you, my father despised them, but mainly because they were so vulgar and corrupt.'

Karl felt awful; he was betraying his family. But Steve seemed fascinated, 'What do you hear from your family now?'

'Only the odd Red Cross message. You know, twenty-five

22

words are allowed and you mustn't add anything; but you can choose phrases like, "I am well", and "How are you". But even they have stopped now, and we haven't heard anything for almost a year.'

Inside himself Karl felt divided: on the one hand it was sad that his father could no longer write to him, and that he had no idea how the rest of the family who had stayed behind in Germany were getting on – since France had been invaded very little news got through. But on the other hand when his father had been able to write Karl had felt oppressed by the daily letters and postcards. There was always advice and exhortation: spend your money wisely, not on chocolates and sweets – easy advice for his father to give – he did not have the agony of seeing penny bars of chocolate in shop windows. Also his father had kept on asking whether he was doing any schoolwork; it was sad, Karl thought, that now he was at a proper school and working hard his father did not know that his errant and lazy son had become a model pupil and spent all his time studying even at the risk of making himself unpopular. 'There is one thing I can't stand,' Harry Pring had said, looking at Karl meaningfully, 'and that's a swot. For God's sake get out of the study and play about a bit. No wonder you are useless at games, you never practise with a ball.'

Steve however was still thinking about the Jews, in particular the position of German Jews. 'It seems to me that persecution has made the Jews feel unique and chosen; in the same way that a sense of being worthless can separate a boy from others. You see, if you punish a boy he feels unworthy and cut off. He can't do his work or relate to his fellow pupils.'

Karl thought that this was certainly true of Axford. Everyone hated him, and Karl himself found it very hard to be sympathetic to him. Yet here was Steve saying something that he was beginning to understand. Was Steve asking him to be nice to Axford? Surely that was too much to ask. On the other hand, Steve was not just telling him off for not controlling his class during prep; Karl had a feeling that his question about being a Jew had something to do with Vanessa's ideas about the importance of being able to 'connect'.

Ben was interested in the conversation and Karl told him that he felt unsure what Steve had really meant. 'Why can't he come out plainly and tell me what he wants me to do, instead of having long conversations about my family, belonging, and punishment and Judaism.'

'Well, you didn't cope very well, did you? Axford made you take him to Steve, and you forced Steve to back you up when he does not believe in the conventional school punishments. He has been trying to abolish caning for ages, and the old guard, both on the staff and among the senior prefects, is dead against him. It really *is* like the struggle between dictatorship and democracy. And you only resent Steve because of your unresolved oedipal conflicts. You are seeing him as if he was your father and you can't come to terms . . .'

Karl was irritated. 'Go and write your learned paper on the joys of wanking,' he shouted. 'It's simple, isn't it? Either you have order during prep or you have chaos, and I was put there to keep order.'

In the prefects' study the issue was put more simply. Harry Pring, also a new prefect, was for strong measures. 'Steve should have given him a good hiding. That's the trouble with these moderns, all talk. If that tick, Axford, had given me buck I would have socked him right in the kisser and then ordered him a prefects' beating. That would have sorted him out. Of course you and Ben, and Paul and Simon and your other intellectual friends wouldn't like that, but *I* think once you give way you lose all authority.'

Karl had not been in the prefects' study before. In the past, if he'd wanted to speak to a prefect he had had to stand outside and wait. If he had as much as put his head round the door he would have been shouted at. The furniture was old and tatty; the one huge armchair belonged to Douglas by right. Karl was impressed by Douglas. He was due to go into the army shortly, and he was already a lieutenant in the Home Guard. He wore the uniform as often as he could and even had brown leather gloves.

Karl had asked him, very respectfully, whether it would be

24

difficult to get a commission in the army and Douglas had said rather grandly, 'I suppose you need the same sort of quality a good prefect has – a natural authority. And you have got to be fit. I'll be in the Engineers, because my eyesight wasn't good enough for the Air Force.'

'Do you think they will have me?' Karl asked. He had already been refused once for the Home Guard, and thought he would try again. 'I would be prepared to do anything,' he had said on that occasion. 'You must need someone to take messages, or be an interpreter? Surely if the Germans landed, someone would be needed to interpret or something.'

'Sorry,' they had replied, 'but we are not allowed to take aliens into the Home Guard.'

The Air Corps would have been marvellous. Karl had visions of himself in a plane, heroically manning the guns, blasting enemy fighters out of the sky. 'Sorry,' the Air Force officer said, and he looked up at Karl as if he had just prevented a major national disaster, 'We can't have the Germans given a bomber as a present, can we?'

Karl wanted to argue. Surely they must realize that he was much more interested in the defeat of Hitler's Germany than anyone else! But what was the use? Everyone seemed to find it difficult to distinguish his position from that of a 'proper' German. That was the reason, of course, why Axford had annoyed him so much.

Douglas sat in his special chair, lounging elegantly and looking superbly relaxed. He was smoking a Gold Flake cigarette. Karl noticed that, and decided to get a packet as soon as he had some money.

Douglas said, 'I don't know, the house is going to pot again. First there's this business with Axford, a fourth former giving buck; and now Dunning. I think that little bugger has been thieving. Karl and Harry, you haven't attended one of our interrogations have you? We'll wait until later, when they are in bed, and then we will get Dunning up to the study and ask a few questions.'

Karl was delighted; perhaps Douglas would show him how proper English school discipline was to be kept.

'Karl, we need a lamp. Works wonders if you shine a lamp into their eyes.'

Karl had seen something like that in a film. The FBI were interrogating a man. The lamp was shining into his eyes and they all shouted at him until he confessed. Karl felt thrilled; he was a proper prefect now and Douglas was going to show him how to get a confession. Karl knew Dunning, a redfaced boy. His clothes were always very seedy, and it looked as if his parents were not well off.

'Go on, then, get the lamp. It's in the masters' common room. They are having their supper now and no one will see you.' Karl was not too happy about sneaking into the masters' common room, but this was worth it, he thought. He came back, the blackout curtains had already been drawn, a chair had been put in the middle of the room and Dunning was fetched. He came in, looking half-asleep, and not sure what it was all about.

'Sit down here,' Douglas said quietly. 'Now, we want to know what you've been taking from the lockers – quite a lot of tuck is missing. What do you say to that?'

'I've not taken anything, honestly, I haven't. Why did you get me out of bed? I was asleep, you can't do that.'

'Don't you tell us what we can do and what we can't. You are a cheeky little sod and you nick things, everyone knows that.'

'No I don't.'

Karl noticed that the cord on Dunning's dressing gown was frayed and his left knee was jerking up and down.

'We have got witnesses that you've been thieving.'

Dunning came back fiercely, 'Whoever says that is a bloody liar.'

Douglas snarled, 'Don't you dare swear in the prefects' study.'

Karl joined the interrogation. He was excited and enjoying himself. 'Can you *prove* you didn't take anything? Have *you* got witnesses?' Harry Pring joined in. 'Everyone knows you're a thieving little bugger. Come on, admit it.'

'I thought you weren't allowed to swear in the prefects' study,' Dunning retorted.

Harry Pring shrieked with anger. 'He's only a junior and

he's giving buck. Come on, Douglas, let's give him a slippering. We can't cane any more but there's nothing in the rules about the slipper.'

Douglas was cautious. 'In the first place he hasn't admitted anything yet, and in the second I don't think Steve would approve. No, we'd better not.'

'Wallop him all the same. He's a cheeky sod; come on, admit you're a thief.'

'I am not a thief.'

Karl was beginning to feel uneasy. In the beginning it had all been good fun, getting the room ready, being one of the prefects and asking what seemed to him a devastating question. But he did not like the idea of beating Dunning and he admired his courage. He was only one against ten and he did not seem all that frightened. If he had been in Dunning's place he would not have admitted anything, either, but Dunning went further: 'Look here, you have no right to do this to me, you are worse than the Gestapo. I am going to report this to the Head and my parents.' He was nearly crying but he made his point. Douglas was no longer sure of himself.

'Well, let this be a warning. We can't have thieving in the boarding house and we had a report it was you. A lot of tuck has been disappearing lately. Just watch out, if we catch you at it you will be very, very sorry. Now get out.'

Dunning went out and Karl took the lamp back, grateful that no one saw him hurrying into the masters' common room.

'Just like Douglas to leave it to someone else to take all the risks,' he thought.

The next morning Paul, Simon and Ben went for Karl.

'What the hell have you been doing to that kid, Dunning?' Paul asked angrily. When he was angry his temples throbbed and his brown eyes looked really fierce. Karl was particularly fond of Paul. He was very good at English and his essays were handed round. He had a marvellous infectious laugh, a zany shrieky roar that could be heard a long way away. He was popular with all the boarders and he was the chairman of the house-meeting. Steve had instituted a weekly meeting of the boarders where they could say what they liked, make their own decisions and levy their own money. Karl had never seen anything like it and was terribly impressed. This, he thought, was real democracy and he was amazed at how well it all ran. Paul made marvellous speeches and he was deeply disliked by most of the prefects and some of the masters. As Ben put it, 'They suspect that we undermine their authority and up to a point they are right. We have got a forum to express our views, and I bet the teachers are terrified that we might say something critical about them. The old guard and the authoritarians don't like the house-meeting. They are just waiting for a chance to complain and make trouble. Some time ago, before you came, we complained about old Barnes who was always reading the papers we pay for. He was outraged, and went straight to Steve. Steve asked him why he read the boys' papers instead of getting his own, and Barnes stormed out, furious.'

Karl had known that Paul would resent what had happened to Dunning, but then Paul was not a prefect. Karl said, 'It was a decision taken by the prefects. They are worried that there is too much thieving in the house and they wanted to make an example.'

Even as he said it Karl felt that his voice lacked conviction. He found it hard to be too outraged by stealing. In the past he had taken lots of money from his father's pockets; but he had never been caught and he had never had to admit to stealing.

'I like your righteous indignation,' Paul sneered. 'What do you think you have achieved by treating a small boy as if he was a criminal? What about the way you questioned him? It sounds like a Gestapo trial, why didn't you put thumbscrews on him? You might have got a confession.' Paul's indignation rose. '*You* of all people ought to know better. You know about concentration camps and how the rights of people are ignored in them.'

'Christ,' said Karl, 'you don't half go on; on and on and on.'

'I wish you wouldn't use the name of Christ as a term of exasperation or abuse. He happens to be a personal friend to me; you should be careful how you use that word.' Paul was going through an Anglo-Catholic phase and his friends had all been living through his religious doubts and dilemmas.

28

Ben thought this was going too far. 'Don't get too self-righteous, Paul. I know you are in the right, but surely this is a complex situation . . .'

'Complex be damned, it's straightforward. The prefects run a midnight court and question a kid as if they were the secret police. Surely this is just the sort of thing we are trying to stop. Steve stops caning and then this happens. And the worst thing of all is that Karl takes part and even defends it.'

Karl felt hot and guilty. 'It's all right for you to be indignant, but I must keep some sort of order and if I don't have the support of the other prefects I am lost.'

'OK. But just think how that bastard Douglas uses you; you pull the chestnuts out of the fire and he just sits there.'

Karl made a mental note of 'chestnuts out of the fire' – a good phrase, and he decided to use it soon. Not long ago he had said to the matron, the dreaded red-haired, red-eyed and malevolent matron, 'I think that's your pigeon,' and she had remarked, 'Funny how quickly *you people* pick up colloquial English,' and Karl had known she was not being complimentary. Most of the staff congratulated him on how quickly and correctly he had learnt to speak English, but she had spoken rather spitefully.

'Hates us refugees,' Ben had explained, 'thinks we are Steve's little pets and that we get more privileges than the other boys. It's all because I stay with Steve and Vanessa in the holidays. She resents that, thinks I have a special relationship with them, I suppose you catch it indirectly.'

Karl felt a great surge of anger against his father for letting him end up like this. Once upon a time he had been a 'Hartland'. Everyone in Essen had known the family. And now he was 'you people' – a 'foreigner'. He only had to open his mouth and everyone knew he was not English. 'You are not English are you? Where are you from? Essen? Where is that? Isn't that the place that we have just been bombing? What do you think about that? Does it worry you? Where is your family?'

It seemed to Karl that if you were a foreigner, a refugee, people felt entitled to ask you questions; and they always ended up so completely baffled by your replies that they would ignore them and change the subject by saying: 'I once met another refugee; he came from, oh I have forgotten, Frankfurt, I think, ever such a nice person.'

Karl wanted to say, 'There are some Germans I would like bombed from morning till night; but Essen was a nice town and I don't even know if my father is still there. I have not heard from him for months. I hate being a refugee and not belonging anywhere. I can't go into the Air Force, I can't get into the Home Guard, and I must report to the police if I go away from here for more than twenty-four hours. I must not ride a bike further than five miles and if I try to be a good prefect my real friends imply that I am an underground agent for the Gestapo.'

Paul introduced his girl friend to Karl. Everyone knew about Isobel. Ben had told him about her, 'Yes, she is second year sixth, very clever, they are putting her in for a scholarship. I heard Steve say that she was one of the cleverest pupils he had ever taught. I think Paul has done well to get her to go out with him. I mean, normally older girls don't look at younger boys, do they? She is clever, but Paul makes the most of it. All life is a great drama for him, and now it's love in a big way; Christ Almighty, she must get sick of all this adoration. Do you know one night he got up, went to her house, threw pebbles at her window to wake her up and then declared his undying love. What if he'd woken up her landlady? Anyhow, that's Paul, nothing in moderation.'

Harry Pring had described her somewhat differently, 'Oh her, yeah, clever little bitch, always making wisecracks at you. I can't stand these clever dames – I bet she's all right, though.'

Isobel grinned at Karl, 'I've been wanting to meet you for a long time. You're from Germany, aren't you. From Essen? What was it like?'

Karl preferred Isobel's interest which was not quite as superficial as the usual enquiry, but he did not know what to say. To him Essen meant his home in the Alfredstrasse, and a huge willow with sponge-like diseased spots on it in the front garden. 'We must do something about that tree,' his father had said. Or Essen meant his eccentric Aunt Julia who went shopping with a string bag, carrots and things sticking out, her white hair all over the place, grinning at him and making him kiss her stubbly cheek. Or Essen meant his dog, or playing chess with his old grandfather and teasing him and the maids. How could he explain? So he just said, 'It is an industrial town but where we lived you would hardly notice. It was all green and there were many trees.' He tried to put a disparaging tone into his voice. For one thing he knew that in England it was not done to boast, and then if he was too enthusiastic about the place Isobel might think he cared more for Germany than for England and Elmfield.

'What did your father do?'

Again this was a difficult question. Karl's father had been a banker and people immediately assumed that he was a very rich man. To Karl, who had just taken things for granted at home, it did not seem that they were as rich as all that. Isobel laughed when he told her, 'Gosh, a banker, a capitalist beast. Did you have gold plates? We are very poor at home, we only have one room and a bedroom and my mother has to go out to work. What happened to your mother?'

Karl explained that his mother had died three years before he left Germany.

Isobel seemed sad about that and went on, 'Are you happy here?'

Karl had no idea how to answer this either. He liked the questions Isobel asked, but he was not sure how to explain what he really felt. Was he happy? Well, certainly he loved the school, and understood that it represented his one chance not to become a farm labourer. There had only been a few jobs he had enjoyed at the approved school. The pigs weren't too bad and he liked hard work like harvesting or digging. Now he dug in the school garden every Sunday. Steve had made a rule: you either went to church or you dug for victory. Anything was better than church, so Karl and Ben dug on Sundays with Steve and Vanessa. Actually it had not been the hard work at the approved school that had worried him, just the hopelessness. But now everything was different. He was in the sixth form and it looked as if they liked him at the school. He had only two

31

problems: one was being a prefect – a wave of embarrassment shot through him when he thought about that – and the other one was that Steve had told him he could not be a doctor, which was what he had come to believe he would like to be.

'Look, Karl, you are no good at mathematics, but you can do well in English and in history, how about that? Combine them with German and Latin and you may well get to a university – but medicine, no.'

That had been a blow and old Toss, the biology teacher, had taken it badly. Karl was no longer included in the tea parties for favourite boys, when Toss had filled them up with buns, muttering, 'Humph, eat up, boys can eat any amount, go on, eat up.'

Toss was essentially a nice man, he loved boys and knew how to treat them gently, even in an embarrassing situation. He had come in when John and Karl were in the bath together. John had put both feet round Karl's prick and they had shrieked with laughter. Toss had called them in later, 'Humph, if you are in the bath and one of you gets what you, humph, call the horn, don't shout about it, just be quiet about it, no need to shout and let everyone know about it.'

John was furious. Toss had shamed him over something he felt guilty about already, and he wanted Karl to know that he was no worse than anyone else; so all his anger was directed at poor old Toss who really only wanted to be a progressive schoolmaster; 'The dirty old sod, what's it to do with him what we do. Anyhow he can't talk, always tossing himself off.'

Karl thought, 'Who doesn't,' but kept quiet, fascinated by John's tirade.

Karl really liked Toss and he was sorry that when he said he was not going to do science he had lost him as a friend. To make matters worse he was puzzled by history.

'It's easy,' Ben said to him, 'you just get a book on the subject, change it all round a bit and then copy it out and that's your weekly essay.'

Yet was he happy? He felt sad about his family but he did not miss them. It was as if a ton weight had been lifted from him. He had friends and in spite of school rules he felt more free than ever before. But there were many confusions – he wished more than anything that he need not be a foreigner any longer. He wanted to disguise himself with a perfect Oxford accent, a pipe and a commission in His Majesty's forces, a lovely uniform and perhaps the spread wings of a pilot on his chest.

He looked at Isobel and noticed that she had lovely dark eyes, her tongue darted over her teeth and she was smiling at him. Karl said, 'Yes, I really am very happy here.'

Chapter 2

It was nearly time for the holidays. Steve called Karl into his study.

'What are you going to do in the holidays? Now that the worst of the bombing is over in London we want the staff to have proper holidays and we are going to close the boarding house until next term. Can you let me know what your plans are?'

Karl felt quite ill. Holidays had not been such a terrible problem as he had feared while there were massive air raids on London. Everyone had just stayed in the school and it had been marvellous. There were no classes and the boys went for walks and swam in the river. Karl, who still had a lot of catching up to do, found it quite a relief to be able to sit in the library and read without interruptions. Now, suddenly, all this was threatened. But he did not want Steve to know how uneasy he felt, so he said stiffly, 'I'll write to my sister and we will arrange something.' 'Good,' said Steve. 'I'm sure it can't be easy for you as you have no proper home. I wish we could offer you hospitality but we are completely exhausted and have already got Ben with us.'

Karl thought, 'Yes, Ben, it's all right for him, he's able to stay on. Now I'll have to ask my sister for money or get her to find me somewhere to stay. Where, for God's sake? What can I do? Perhaps find a temporary job – who would want me? And in any case I would still need a place . . .'

The end of term was a bad time for rows. Karl had been carving a figure out of scrubbing soap. It looked a bit like

Epstein's Adam but it was a woman. Harry Pring had looked over his shoulder while he was whittling away with his penknife.

'Who is that supposed to be? Isobel? I think I recognize the tits. Working from memory? I bet Paul's had a good feel.'

Karl was outraged; Harry had noticed he liked Isobel – more than liked her. He thought about her a lot and loved it when she talked to him in the library. He had thought of showing her the figure when it was finished. She liked contemporary art and she liked to be modern. Surely this nude would impress her. Remembering the outrage Epstein's Adam had caused, Karl hoped that this, too, would be thought ahead of its time, advanced and daring. Sometimes he saw himself as an artist, facing the world with works that would eventually be an important part of the European heritage. And now that slob Harry Pring was suggesting that Karl's motives were not pure. Karl had disliked Harry for a long time: he was everything Karl secretly would like to have been, good at sports, popular with the games-playing prefects, admired by the small boys. 'Jolly good score on Saturday,' they would shout at him – and he just jauntily touched his cap. Then girls, they crowded round him. They did not even seem to mind the pimples that bloomed on him, with open pussy craters where he had shaved the top off. He danced well, and no girl ever said 'no' to him at the end-of-term dance. This had happened to Karl and he had felt like crawling into a hole. The only thing Harry was not good at was school work.

'It's all boring and I can't stand swots like you and that Ben and Paul. You must be mad just sitting there. Who cares? I'll be in the Air Force soon and then off we go.'

And now Harry was insulting not only Karl's soap carving but Isobel. Karl looked at Harry and thought, 'I can get him on the floor in no time. He may be good at games but I can get him. There is no one in the study so now is the time to settle up.'

He rushed at Harry, disgusted at being so near to the pussy face; he twisted him round and when he had him on the floor, sat firmly on him. Karl remembered that, at a party when he was a very small boy, Kurt Spiegel had farted into his face when he sat on him, but that was a bit crude. He also considered gobbing into Harry's face, but gave up the idea when he remembered that this was, after all, the prefects' study. So he just let him wriggle and get angrier.

'Wait till I get you, you German swot.'

'So I'm a German swot, am I?' Karl was bursting with anger but not quite sure what to say. To him the English were so marvellous that he could not simply retaliate with something like, 'You English fool!' He had come across the word 'pimp', and liked it because it combined pimples with a disgraceful activity, but abuse did not come all that easily so he just got off Harry and said, 'Next time I'll knock you out.'

In Germany Karl had been taught how to fight and had loved his boxing lessons. He had never told anyone that he could box quite scientifically – but didn't do much of it because hitting people hurt his hand. He rather hoped that Harry would assume that he could not fight just because he was unable to play cricket. But Harry did not want to go any further, although he was furious.

This fight changed their relationship. Up to that time Harry had inducted Karl into school life, 'This is matron – we call her Crackle', 'This is Old Conc, we always play him up', 'No one takes any notice of old Eggo'. And whenever Karl could not understand what Harry was saying he shouted at him, 'Why don't you learn some English; you spend enough time swotting.'

But now Karl had shown not only that he was stronger but that he could do without Harry. As Harry picked himself up Karl shouted at him, 'You can just go to hell! And don't call me German; I am not a German!'

Harry stormed out of the room and they did not speak to each other again until the next morning.

'Sorry I called you a German yesterday.'

'Oh that's all right, I am sorry I got so angry.'

Karl liked this exchange, it was all part of what he had understood to be 'fair play' – you had a fight and you made it up. He did not like Harry any better but they had ended the row.

At break Karl went into the study. He had a free period and he intended to get on with carving his soap figure. He loved the smell of the soap and the way it acquired a particular patina the longer he handled it. The figure still stood on his shelf, but as he came close to it he saw that her head had been knocked off and a matchstick pushed up her bottom. Karl did not immediately know what to do. He wanted to sit down and cry, but he knew he could not do that. Nothing could have been worse for his reputation. If the fourth form found out that he had sat down and 'blubbed' he would never be able to keep them under control. So he rushed to the lavatory, and sat there. He could not cry, no tears would come but he just sat there, shattered. He told Paul later. Paul was very indignant,

'It's the games louts again, they can't stand any form of culture. They should all be on the other side in this war. I'm sorry, Karl, it was a beautiful little figure. Perhaps it can be put together? The sooner that lot leave the better it will be for the school. They just destroy anything beautiful or decent.'

He went for Douglas, 'Were you responsible for destroying Karl's soap figure?'

Douglas looked a bit embarrassed, 'Can't anyone take a joke round here? Come on, we just stuck a match up its arse, so what, it's only soap, what's all the fuss about. I thought it was a disgusting little figure, all those tits and that big arse, it was meant as a joke, wasn't it, Karl?'

Karl felt he could not really attack Douglas. He saw Harry Pring in the background, grinning, so he only said, 'It doesn't matter any more, you have spoilt it. Let's just throw it away, it can't be mended.'

Douglas put his arm round Karl's shoulders, 'Sorry, old man, I didn't know it meant all that much to you. It was meant to be a joke; Harry thought it would be funny, didn't you, Harry?'

Harry went very red and muttered that he had to see Crackle about his suitcase.

The depression about the soap figure merged with Karl's feelings about the holidays. His sister had written to him and told him that she had found a room near hers and that it was nice and cheap. She told him to go straight to her flat and wait for her to come home from work. She would leave the key under the mat. Margot was doing war work. She was not much of a letter-writer, but Karl gathered that she was welding pieces of metal together to go into aeroplanes. Anyhow, she had written, it was better than being a housemaid and she liked the people she was working with.

Excitement about the holidays was mounting. Bucko Harris gave a graphic account of what he planned to do. 'We go to this nightclub, it stays open late and they let me drink as many Green Goddesses as I want. That's the drink for me, brandy, creme de menthe and orange. Fantastic. With that inside you, you really dance.'

He clutched his hand to his stomach, shut his eyes as if he was holding his partner really tight and shuffled round the room. 'There's this barmaid, incredible tits, you can see them right through her blouse. Last time I was there she went outside with a Canadian and when she came back I said to her, "I know what you have been up to." She went mad, but I could tell, you could see her nipples standing up; they do that when they get all excited. I'll take her outside this time, you never know your luck, do you?'

Ben was coldly contemptuous. 'He is pathetic. Do you know, his mother works in a pub. They make the poor little sod sit in the backroom and he has nowhere to go; and the mother has all sorts of men staying with her. That's why he is here – his home is so bad; I heard the Steves talking about it. He just shows off and pretends he is having a wonderful time.'

Karl suddenly hated Ben, 'You have no emotions, you are just like an amoeba; that's right an amoeba, you have no feelings, you just stand by and observe and collect facts.'

Ben was hurt, 'You *are* ratty, it must be the end of term. You're jealous of me because I am staying behind and you have to go into the unknown, you hate leaving the security of the womb.'

Karl had been reading E. M. Forster. 'Well, at least it is a womb with a view. I hate you but you are probably right. It is just that one can't stand it all the time. You seem to feel you have to set yourself up as our resident psychiatrist. No, you are right, I hate the thought of the holidays. I suppose I will find a library where I can work and I can go to the theatre. I did not get on too well with my sister when we were children. It was better once we left Germany but she still thinks she is in charge of me and she can be very bossy. To make matters worse she has a real obsession about money. Do you know, all the time it's, "Save your money, don't be like your dreadful Uncle Eric." He was the family wastrel it seems; it is terrible how members of your family are used as sticks to beat you with. Yes, I am off families, specially my own.'

Then they had argued about 'detachment'. Ben thought how good it would be not to have ordinary emotions but to stand apart from the world and to observe and report. Karl had hated the idea, and yet he also felt that if only he could be 'detached' and not become involved he would be saved from much pain. All relationships, they had agreed, bring suffering, and families stifle the individual; all the troubles of society can be attributed to the family, that's where it all starts.

'When we get on the bus for London, let's all wear our prefects' caps,' urged Harry Pring.

'Yeah, they'll think we are some secret branch of the Polish cavalry, no one has seen caps like these before – yeah, all the tarts will let us have a go for nothing,' rhapsodized Bucko Harris.

Harry Pring gave a shrill shriek, 'Canaanin.'

He had taught Karl this and told him it was a sort of secret rallying cry. 'It really means, "Are you going to have it in?" ' Harry confided, 'But you can't say that, so it's "Canaanin" and no one knows what we mean. Stupid erks. I said it to Stinker in class and he just looked puzzled and everyone else pissed themselves laughing.'

John seemed in agonies, 'For God's sake someone lend us a fag, I am dying for one. I'll pay you back after the hols.'

Karl, had he had any cigarettes, would have given one to John, but he was now the owner of a pipe and he was getting better at smoking it. At first the acid dribble had made him almost sick. It had felt as if the lacquer from the inside of the bowl was coating his throat, but he had stuck it out and watched Steve carefully so that by now he could keep his pipe alight quite a long time and could look contemplative and serious as he puffed out the smoke.

Harry and his followers shouted 'Canaanin' at every woman

between eight and eighty they saw on the road. Paul was sitting next to Karl, 'Honestly, I wish to God I didn't have to travel with this bunch of hooligans. They go on as if they had been released from a prison. School is not as bad as all that; they're just louts.'

'Louts' was a word Steve used a lot. It covered all behaviour he did not approve of: eating in the streets, shouting, holding hands with girls in public, and not greeting masters politely was 'loutish', and Paul was right, the behaviour on the bus was surely loutish.

Paul was cross and Karl could see his cheek muscles undulating with anger. 'Come on, Karl, you're a prefect now, stop this behaviour. Tell Bucko to stop shouting about that brothel he seems to live in and that ghastly Pring from singing, "I'm coming, I'm coming for my prick is getting sore." '

'Is it to the tune of Men of Harlech?' Karl asked.

When the coach reached London Karl had to make his way by tube to Maida Vale where his sister Margot lived. He had not travelled by tube before but he found the maps quite helpful once his initial panic had subsided. He noticed that lines of metal beds stretched along the platform at every station, and although it was late morning people were still sitting on their bunks. Outside the tube station he became really frightened. The street where his sister lived had been bombed; the first houses were just piles of rubble and as he was walking along where the houses still stood he noticed the hardboard covers over the window spaces and the dust. His sister's house was completely intact except that most of the windows were gone. Karl thought the house looked like a blind man with dark glasses. But at least it was still standing. He went up the stairs, found the key and let himself into the room. It wasn't a flat really, just a room with a small cooker. The furniture was dark brown and very shabby. In the middle of the room, in complete contrast, was a beautiful Persian rug. At home it had lain between the salon and the drawing-room, but now it seemed quite out of place in the half-dark room. What light there was came in through some of the windows which had been replaced with glass, others were just hardboard. Karl had always taken his sister for granted, not that he liked her all that much but she was there, and he had to admit she had done a great deal for him. Once when he was little, they had both been on a roundabout at a fair. It had thrown him all over the place and he had fallen off his seat and she had pulled him back. Karl had been certain that he was about to be chewed up by the gearwheels and had been terribly frightened. He could not quite understand why she had not pushed him off the seat in the first place considering how he was always teasing her, tripping her up and making his terrible magic faces. He had thanked her profusely. 'Thank you, thank you, Margot, you have saved my life,' and she had just shrugged her shoulders and said, 'Oh, don't go on like that, it's not that important.' Perhaps, Karl had thought, she was already regretting her generous action. And then she had saved him from the approved school camp; she had gone to Steve and asked him to take her brother and she had written to the other Hartlands in New York for some money. They had left England some time before Karl had got out of Germany and they had taken all their money with them. They had left their beautiful house by the lake in Germany, and all those paintings, but they were still rich by any standard and they had agreed to pay for Karl's schooling. It would never have occurred to him that they might. He owed being at Elmfield to Margot and her persistence.

Karl looked into a small store cupboard by the gas ring. There was not much in it, just a tin of pilchards. They were obviously for him because he knew Margot hated fishy things. Then he heard her bouncing up the stairs. She was wearing her working clothes, a dirty pair of dungarees and a turban which was knotted on top of her head. Her hair was invisible. 'She looks like an Easter egg with giftwrapping round it,' Karl thought. She was much thinner, there was dirt round her eyes and she looked irritable.

'Hallo, baby brother, bunny rabbit.'

'Oh, Christ, there she goes again, trying to make me small and babyish,' Karl thought crossly.

She grinned and seemed pleased to see him. 'God, you've grown again, you're a giant — at least by the standards of our family. Father was only as tall as me and look, you are a head taller now and you are thin. God, can you remember how repulsively fat you were?'

Karl wished she wouldn't remind him of that. He had hated being a fat boy, everyone used to get at him. The gym master at school, his sister and even Mutti used gently to restrain him as he rammed yet another breadroll into his mouth.

Margot went on briskly, 'I'll tell you what we must do now; I'll take you to see your new landlady, Mrs Hodge. It isn't very marvellous but it's only ten shillings a week. You can wash and get ready to register with the police and I'll clean up here. You can use this room during the day; you have got school work to do, haven't you?'

Karl had Taylor's *Medieval Mind* in his bag and also Huizinga's *Waning of the Middle Ages*. Steve had told him to read them in the holidays and had lent him his own copies.

'Then I'll take you to the police station. You have got your alien's book, haven't you?'

Karl felt irritated that she immediately assumed he had forgotten the little grey book. It had his picture in it, and whenever he was going away from Elmfield he had to report to the police station there before he left and then again at the nearest police station when he arrived.

'We go to the Edgware Road Station. The sergeant there is used to refugees. He is very nice really.'

Karl remembered how the police in Germany had snapped at him, 'Take your hat off. This isn't a Jew school.' And he had only put that stupid hat on because his father had made him wear it. Margot was right; the police in England were kindly and they never snapped or made him wait unnecessarily.

'Then we'll go down the road and see Alice and her cousin Gerd. They are my best friends here. I don't know what I would have done without Alice. She is a bit noisy and bossy but she has a heart of gold. Do you know I was really ill once, and I had to go hospital? It was Alice who looked after me then and came to see me.'

Karl was upset that his sister had been ill and that he had not been told.

'What could you have done? Anyhow, I want you to get on with your schooling. About tonight; there is Gerd. You have to shout a bit, he has a hearing aid and when the battery plays up it squeaks. Don't take any notice, he is a bit self-conscious about it. His ear got bad when they hit him on the head in the concentration camp at Oranienburg, outside Berlin. Come on, I'll take you to your lodgings.'

They walked down the road till they came to a few houses less damaged than the ones near the tube station, and went down the steps of one and into the basement. Margot pulled the bell. Mrs Hodge appeared. She was hugely shapeless and wore an overall that was black with grease down both sides. Her slippers were trodden right down at the back and her stockings draped over them. She looked over her glasses.

Margot said, 'This is my little brother; the one who'll be staying with you for the holidays.'

Karl was furious, 'There she goes again; *little brother*. I am a head taller than her.'

Mrs Hodge looked up, grinned, said ' 'Allo' very loudly and asked Karl to follow her. He was fascinated by the curlers in her hair. He had never seen anything like it before. The basement smelt of cat's piss and grease and it was dark.

'They won't put the bleeding windows back, I've been to see them but it's the same old story. "There's a war on." "I know there's a war on," I said, "but I need to see, don't I?" This is my son, Mr Hodge.'

Mr Hodge was quite old. He reminded Karl of Quasimodo in *The Hunchback of Notre Dame*. One eye was turned upwards, he was hunchbacked and he seemed to walk sideways. He was smoking a thin cigarette, all floppy, hanging down from his tobacco stained mouth.

'This is the college boy.'

Mrs Hodge shouted a bit louder when she talked to her son. He grinned and looked at Karl but Mrs Hodge went on, 'Yes, I wish you had studied. There's nothing like an education.'

She waved her hand dismissively at her son. 'Him, they wouldn't even have him in the pioneer corps. I don't mind, let them get on with it, that's my motto. But he just sits here doing nothing except rolling himself fags. Did a bit of rescue work when they bombed us, it was terrible.'

Karl was gratified that not only had she called him a college boy and envied his education, but she had said nothing about his foreign accent. His room contained a huge double bed, a wash-stand and a chair. It smelt of cats even more than the hall.

'You'll be comfortable here,' said Mrs Hodge. 'This is Liberty Hall, you just come and go as you please and I'll bring you a lovely breakfast in bed.'

Karl had not brought many things with him and he left his clothes in the case so that they would not get dirty. He decided to put his handkerchief over the pillow and hoped he would not smell of cats when he came out of the basement. He counted his money. He had made four pounds teaching Canadian soldiers German. He had not told Margot about this money, it was his and he had earned it. Every Sunday for some weeks the Canadians had come into the school. They were huge, cheerful men who did not seem to give a damn for anybody. All the locals were afraid of them. They called Karl 'Prof'. 'Say, Prof,' one of them had asked, 'What's the German for fucking? That's what we'll need to know when we get there – not all this crap about "Wo ist der Bahnhof? Where's the station?".'

Karl was amazed how they talked about their army. To him the greatest and best thing would be to join the Forces and fight against the Germans. No one would let him, but that was his dream, to ride into Essen on a tank, take the surrender of the town, and then on to the Gymnasium. He had a few scores to settle with the masters there. They would be standing against the wall, the director, Herr Kosch, Ivan the Terrible, and they would say, 'That's the Hartland boy, not much good at school, but look at him now, in charge of a tank. Please, Herr Hartland, we are sorry, we did not mean it . . .'

But the Canadians had said to him, 'Don't join the army, Prof. It's a load of shit. You stay here, son, get an education, that's what you need . . .'

Back in Margot's room he found her looking much more cheerful. 'It's Friday, thank God, I have been doing overtime

44

for months. Look, I'll paint my legs and then we'll go to Alice's.'

Stockings were scarce and instead Margot put some dye stuff on her legs. It was brownish yellow and Karl thought it was almost as good as real stockings. He showed Margot his report from the school.

'This is good, baby bunny. Very nice. On Sunday when we have lunch with the Levis we'll take this along and show it to them. You don't know them, but he is your Aunt Eunice's brother. He was a banker in Berlin, stinking rich, not just rich but really rich. He handles his sister's affairs in this country and he pays all your bills for you. So you'd better behave.'

'What does she think I'll do,' thought Karl crossly, 'piss on the table?'

'We'll show them the report and they'll see that they are not wasting their money. This is better than your German reports – do you remember?'

Karl remembered only too well. He remembered the time he had tried to forge his father's signature on a school report return slip, because the report was a bad one and he did not want his father to be worried by seeing it. Then he had made a mess of the signature, tried to take the first attempt out with a chemical ink remover and made a hole in the paper. His father had had to ask him for the report.

Karl blushed at the memory of this disgraceful episode, and he was sure Margot was thinking of it as well, but all she said was, 'These are even better reports than I had.'

'Yes, you always were a good girl at school.'

'And a fat a lot of good it did me. Now your sister is the most distinguished welder on Staple's Corner – come on, let's go to Alice's.'

Alice was wearing a black dress, quite deeply cut with a piece of lace covering a very ample bosom. She had thick eye lids and a huge mouth, and Karl noticed that some lipstick had smudged on to her teeth. She roared, 'Ah, this is the beautiful brother, not so little, is he? What lovely fair hair,' and she grabbed Karl's hair and ruffled it. 'Lovely to be young and have a lot

45

of hair, all nice and silky. What a gorgeous boy, I could eat you.'

Karl was slightly taken aback, although it was nice to be thought beautiful and to be admired for the hair on his head. He was terrified of getting bald. Once a barber had leant over him confidentially, 'Going to get thin on top soon, how about some of this lotion.'

Karl had spent ages aligning two mirrors so that he might examine the back of his head to see if there were any bald spots.

Alice shouted, 'Yes, that's a lovely young man, looks a proper Englishman, doesn't he. I think he needs "educating", though. I think I should take him in hand.'

Karl realized she meant sex and he cringed inwardly. He was desperate to find a nice, kind mistress. But her, God, not her. He felt like covering his genitals with his hands and crossing his legs at the same time. Did she mean it? Margot came to the rescue.

'You leave my little brother alone; anyhow, he is in love, he has got a girlfriend in Elmfield. Isobel, isn't it?'

Karl was torn between gratitude and fury. In his letters to his sister he had exaggerated his relationship with Isobel and made out that it was deep and real, whereas all he did was to worship Isobel from a distance. He was happy when she just talked to him in the library. Anyhow, it was his secret and there she was, blurting it all over the place. He looked at Alice sideways. She wasn't ugly but she seemed very old to him and she had a very hairy upper lip. Alice shouted on, 'Meet Cousin Gerd.'

He had a nice smile. Very deep, dark eyes and a melancholic look. He was quite bald. Karl noticed his fine quality suit. His own was wearing badly and he noticed other people's clothes. This was surely a German suit, the cut was different from English ones. Gerd shook Karl's hand. 'Ah, this is our Englishman, yes, you have become properly acclimatized. It's so much easier if you are young. I am studying English all the time, a fascinating language, but speaking it presents problems, it's possibly because I am slightly deaf . . .'

46

'What do you mean "slightly"?' Alice bawled. 'My love, you are properly *chairish*. Karl, do you know what *chairish* means?'

Karl knew that it was Hebrew or Yiddish for deaf; he knew that much, at least. He was not quite sure whether to speak German or English but decided to stick to German. Gerd, Alice, and his sister's English seemed quite gruesome to him. They mixed German, English, and Yiddish words together. Gerd went on. He had obviously taken Alice's crack about his deafness as a great joke.

'We must talk about a number of things that puzzle me and about which I need your advice. You see, I meet so few real English people, and one can't just go up to a gentleman in the library and say – how do you pronounce . . .'

'Heard the latest refugee story?' asked Alice. 'A Berliner says, "Now the English have got me really confused; it's bad enough with Worcester Sauce and Cockburn, but I've just seen a poster saying *Gone with the Wind* pronounced success".'

Gerd came back to his study of English. 'Do you know, when I came out of Oranienburg – that was a concentration camp – I said to myself, "Gerd, you must get out and you must learn English." I had been the editor of a scientific journal. I knew scientific terms, but not the English that is spoken in England. In England they interned me, and the internees made fun of me in the camp – I was let out again very soon, though, but at the concert they sang a rhyme about me:

> Gerd for English examination sits
> He even studies while he shits.

Yes, I really mixed with the crème de la crème there.'

Alice said, 'It was hard for Gerd. He was really spoilt at home. He never even knew what it meant to get his own shirt out of a drawer; the maid did it for him. I still remember him in his office, all grand behind the desk . . .'

'That reminds me,' said Margot, 'do you know what the Dachshund said to the terrier?'

'No, what?'

'At home I was a St Bernard.'

Alice called them to supper. 'It's boiled sausage, I bet you

47

don't get that at school. Just that dreadful English muck. I mean they are marvellous at queueing and they are brave; but, God, their food! Do you get those little sausages with bread and pepper in them? I can't imagine how they dare to call them sausages at all. Mind you, it was hard to get this boiling ring. I had to go to Eberhard's and queue. Do you know that *chonte* (whore) who serves there, she says to me, "Are you a regular?" The *chutzpah*, I have been going there for years. So I said, "What do you want? My fingerprints?" It's bad enough having to stand around for extra food, and then to be questioned! And we need that little bit extra. Gerd works hard, *schleps* himself through the city selling those advertisements. I think they buy from him because they realize he is used to better work. Anyhow, dig in, good *yontef*, can you smell the garlic, it's lovely, it stinks a pleasure.'

Gerd seemed unhappy with his piece of sausage. 'Do you know, Karl, this sausage reminds me of Oranienburg – it's odd, isn't it, how food reminds you of other things; as in Proust, you remember, those biscuits.'

Karl felt flattered that Gerd assumed he had read Proust, which he hadn't. Gerd went on, 'Yes, boiled sausage and the KZ (Concentration Camp). They let me out just before Christmas – this was at the beginning, they wanted to frighten us so they said "if you aren't out within twenty-four hours we will arrest you again." Anyhow, I was in the camp and my release pass came through. It was just before Christmas, as I said, and one of the old communists came up to me. He had been there since '33. I really admired the communists in the camp, they knew what they were in for and they believed in something. With us, well, everyone despised us soft Jewish intellectuals. The guards went for us, specially anyone with glasses, but they had some respect – if that is the right word – for communists because they had ideals, they wouldn't give an inch some of them. So this old communist comes up to me and says, "Man, Gerd, you are going now? Before Christmas? There is boiled sausage at Christmas, are you going to miss that?" That's how it was for him, he had been there so long, a piece of boiled sausage was all that mattered. Well, dig in, *bon appetit.*'

48

They wanted to know what the food at the school was like. Karl had decided, until he was presented with this lovely dinner, that food really did not matter. It was part of the detachment from worldly things that Ben had talked about. It was quite easy to be detached from school food. Generally Karl thought there was not quite enough and he envied the boys who got food parcels from home, but he did not want to say anything about that here in case Margot thought he was hinting, and he could see quite well that life was not easy for her either.

Gerd said, 'You don't know how lucky you are to be studying. I wish I had that chance again. To sit down and to read Tolstoy from cover to cover, Goethe – do you read Goethe?'

Karl said he was reading some for his Higher School Certificate but was not very enthusiastic. He wanted to forget his German and be completely English, but here he was talking German happily and enjoying German food.

Alice turned to Karl again, 'You seem dreamy and romantic, are you in love with that, what was her name, Isobel? When I was your age, and it is not as long ago as you seem to think, I thought about nothing else.'

Gerd turned the conversation to a more impersonal plane. 'I think the theme of young love is wonderfully discussed in *The Sufferings of the Young Werther*. You should look at it.'

Alice sounded sharp. 'Yes, with Gerd the theory always comes before the practice, a pity.'

The conversation turned to food again. 'The only decent bread is at Grodchinsky's. They have wonderful rye bread and even pumpernickel – you know what that is, don't you, Karl? Did they eat it in your part of the world?'

Karl remembered the dark, sweetish bread and how his grandfather had said rapturously, 'A slice of pumpernickel, a slice of white bread, thick butter and in between a thin slice of Westphalian ham, that's very good, you know.'

Gerd wanted the conversation to be more intellectual. 'When I compare the conditions in Germany during the First World War and here in the Second. Really, I find it is much better in England.'

Alice joined in. 'If only they could make a decent cup of

49

coffee. Coffee isn't rationed, you can get as much as you like, but do you know how they make coffee in my office? They put the ground coffee on top of boiling milk!'

They all groaned with horror.

'Cups of tea, yes, cups of tea all the time. I can't stand all this tea business. "Milk?" they ask; "Sugar?" they ask; who cares? And it's always teatime; they don't work properly, not what we used to call work.'

'The rationing system here,' Gerd continued undeterred, 'is a supreme example of the English sense of fair play. I am always amazed how well they treat us. They did not have to take us, but they give us the same amount of food as everyone else. If only the ordinary people could tell the difference between us and the Nazis! If they could, I might not have been interned.'

He turned to Margot. 'The Hoffman boy, did you know him? He went down with the *Andorra Star*. Karl did you hear about that? They put internees, both proper Nazis and Jewish refugees on the same boat to take them to Canada. This was just before they thought there was going to be an invasion, and the boat was torpedoed.'

He changed the subject abruptly, but went on talking to Karl, 'Do you know, I met your father once, a very distinguished gentleman.'

Karl was desperately interested. He so wanted to find out what his father had been like. Once, in the dormitory, the boys had talked about their parents and Paul had said how much he detested his father. 'He is a brute, you have no idea how he treats my mother. There are times when I wish he'd leave us. I can't stand him around the house, wearing nothing but a vest with all his foul black chest hairs sticking out like a big ape's.'

Karl had been amazed. He had been irritated by his father at times, but would never have talked about him like that. And yet, now that he was free of him, he felt a sense of relief, and at the same time guilty because he did not miss him more. People often said to him, 'Don't you miss your family?' and Karl would have liked to say, 'Frankly no,' but instead he put on an embarrassed and pained air so that he would be left alone.

All the same he didn't want to forget what his father was like. He remembered a man with thick black eyebrows. Karl had been a bit scared of him, but he had made good jokes and had bought him an air gun and a dog; and even when he was cross with him he never resorted to stupid punishments. It was bad enough to be in disgrace when he had done something awful.

'You look a bit like father,' Margot had said, and then immediately modified the statement, 'Not entirely, though, there's mother's side, too. Your nose and chin and your colouring, except that mother had red hair.'

So Karl desperately wanted to know more from Gerd. He seemed to be a man with intellectual interests and he might be able to help.

'Tell me what he was like,' Karl asked.

'A very distinguished man. He had wide interests, and was widely read. You could talk with him about any topic under the sun. He was serious, though, and it was not easy to get to know him. I was sure he was completely devoted to his family.'

That wasn't his father either. Karl was disappointed with Gerd's stereotyped picture. He remembered Ben had said, 'Your trouble, Karl, is that you have no father figure to identify with. You can't face up to your oedipal feelings about your father, and you pretend you did not hate him. Your vague memory of him is a protective device.'

Karl, as so often, had been troubled by Ben's instant psychoanalysis. 'Honestly Ben, we should pay you half our pocket money,' he had laughed, to hide his anxiety that Ben might be right.

Alice brought them back to the present. 'You are all looking sad and miserable and it's Friday evening. My old father, may God rest his soul, would have said, "*Schabbes,* a time for joy, the family is together".'

When they got to her door Margot said to Karl, 'See you in the morning, baby brother. Don't forget your alien's book. You have to register, and on Sunday we have a posh lunch at the Levis'.'

In bed Karl felt utterly miserable. The bed smelt of what he

51

hoped was not the late Mr Hodge. He was certain the sheets had not been changed since his death and it was cold. He blew down the sheets to get warm. In the morning Mrs Hodge brought him his breakfast on a tray. 'Here you are, dear, you must work hard all the time. You need spoiling, so here is your breakfast.'

It consisted of three slices of bacon, sausages that had been cooked until they were dark brown, dried out sticks, fried bread and an egg. An egg! And he had not even given her his ration book. Karl folded the bacon into the thick slices of white bread and the world seemed a better place.

Chapter 3

'Let's comb your hair; we must have a tidy baby brother, mustn't we?' Margot reached up with a pocket comb and went through Karl's hair. He would have liked to hit her, but instead he bent forward and let her comb him.

'You made a very good impression on Alice and Gerd,' Margot went on, 'they think you are ever so intelligent. Now try to do it again. Be nice, it really matters here.'

They were standing just outside the Levis' house where they had been invited for Sunday lunch. Margot had on her best grey costume, the one she had been wearing when she left Essen for Elmfield.

'That's the thing about a really good classical costume, it never dates and it looks right anywhere. Do you know, when I got off the train and was met by my future employer, Mrs Randolph, she was wearing exactly the same costume. That must have cheered her up no end! Her new third maid arriving in an identical outfit with two cabin trunks full of clothes. No wonder she was always a bit suspicious of me.'

Margot looked at Karl's suit, 'It really looks a bit shabby by now, but what can we do? You keep on growing and your arms stick out. I asked Alice. She thinks we could get clothes for you at the Woburn House.'

Karl cringed inwardly, 'Now I am going to be bought charity clothes. Just imagine, begging for my clothes. I think I'd rather look ridiculous in these.' But he wished his tie did not have to be the school tie he wore every day. It was thin and the knot had become very small.

The Levis' house stood in a very quiet road, slightly hilly, mock Tudor. Karl recognized the style and remembered Ben's verse for a literary competition:

> What could be cruder than mock Tudor
> like disease venereal on road arterial.

Gerd had talked of the Levis. 'Yes, Walter Levi, there is a smart man. He got out in time and managed to take his money with him. Lafayette and Kornhauser, one of the more important private banks, bigger even than the one belonging to the Hartlands in Essen. It was an international concern. Yes, Walter Levi, we belonged to the same tennis club. Of course that was years ago, he wouldn't have known who I was. A bit of a snob, I remember, always mixing with the top people, really something of a tycoon. Of course you are distantly related to his sister, aren't you? She married your uncle, didn't she?'

Walter Levi appeared at the door and ushered them in. He had very good manners; as he moved them along the hall he seemed to be trying to make them feel they were doing him a favour.

'Ah, you found the house. The bus came all right? These days one can't really rely on public transport.'

He appeared to assume that Karl and Margot had a private limousine tucked away somewhere and only used the buses because they were patriots. Karl noticed Walter's clothes: his cashmere sweater, an expensive-looking foulard tie – the sort of clothes Karl had seen in shop windows in Bond Street. His flannel trousers were superbly creased. He was informally dressed but the clothes were right for the occasion. He was almost bald and the hair that remained was cut very short. He had large, dark, rather sad eyes and a thin, rather sharp nose. Karl noticed little areas of inflamed skin just below his collar. He smelt nice of some very expensive hair tonic. He spoke German elegantly, whatever he said had a slightly witty, ironic edge to it, and he addressed Karl and his sister as if they were very special.

'You must come and meet the children.'

54

An uneasy-looking couple of children rose up, the girl blushed and the boy looked miserable.

'They have been so looking forward to meeting members of the Hartland family.'

The girl was introduced as Hannah. She giggled and withdrew to her chair. Fred did not look too pleased that there were intruders into the home.

Walter introduced Fred. 'He goes to boarding school as well; you two should have a lot to talk about. And Hannah goes to the school down the road. Not all that enthusiastic about it, are you?'

Neither showed much desire for conversation and Karl felt he ought to say something.

'A Canaletto?' he asked, looking at a painting on the wall.

Walter was pleased. 'Ah, you noticed it; you are interested in art? Actually it is a Guardi. Look at the waves and the sky. It has not got the stillness of a Canaletto. It is one of my favourite paintings and I was lucky to get it out, away from the Nazis.' His voice became very quiet, with a confidential undertone. 'I bought it in Switzerland, just before I was thinking of emigrating. Unfortunately there is not much of a market in Guardis – a large number of rather good forgeries has depressed the market, but this one is all right. I have had it checked and it has a genuine pedigree.'

Karl wanted to know what sort of pedigree.

'You follow its history. You see who has bought the painting over the years, to whom it was sold. Then, of course, there are details which tell you: the wood, the quality of the paint. Do you know forgers shoot pellets into the wood to make it look worm-eaten? I am pleased that you are interested in art, though; of course it is not surprising considering your family background. Come, I'll show you the garden, there is time before lunch.'

Karl was amazed to see that the house had its own air raid shelter. No need, then he thought, for the Levis to go down the tube station. It was a very solid construction. Mr Levi explained. 'Yes, when the war was about to break out I sent for a builder and asked him, "Can you make it really bombproof?"

And he said, "Well, if it's a direct hit you won't be there to complain, will you?" We had my mother to stay with us when the raids were bad. Hannah was at her best then. She said to my mother, "Granny, you'll leave your jewels in the shelter all the time, won't you, in case you get hit outside?" It frightened my poor mother out of her wits and we could hardly get her to leave the shelter. Full of lovely remarks, aren't we?' and he passed his hand through Hannah's hair, taking no notice as she squirmed and giggled.

Karl approached Fred, 'Are you specializing in history?'

'Yes.'

'Which period?'

'The Tudors.'

'So am I. Do you find them interesting?'

Fred thought, then shrugged his shoulders, and Karl felt despairingly that a fast flowing and stimulating conversation was not very likely. To his and everyone else's relief the housekeeper appeared. She was a very thin, upright lady, with beautiful blue eyes and very white hair. Somehow she looked much more like a duchess than a housekeeper.

Walter Levi introduced her, 'And this is our Frauelein von Seydlitz. I really don't know what we would do without her.'

There was a suppressed snort from Hannah, just audible. It would seem that she at least had a pretty good idea of what she might do without her. Frauelein von Seydlitz heard it and gave her a long, hostile stare. Then she said stiffly, 'Should we have lunch now?' Not, Karl noticed, 'lunch is served', as a grand butler might have said. There was nervousness and a suggestion of familiarity in her voice. It was almost as if she were begging them, please to be so kind as to have some lunch. Walter Levi introduced Karl and Margot.

'These are the Hartland children from Essen. Margot – she is doing war work and Karl is at Elmfield, he is at exactly the same stage as our Fred, and he is interested in art. I wish my children were.'

The furniture in the dining room was Georgian, and Karl noticed the heavy and ornate silver on the table. Each place was laid with a little mat and there were linen napkins.

When they were sitting down Walter Levi said, 'Of course we are lucky, my sister sends us food parcels. Every fortnight a parcel comes from America. I have said to her, please stop awhile, there is enough to eat here. We have dried eggs and spam – but she keeps on. Do you know these spoilt brats complain when there is tinned meat? I must tell you something. Some friends came to London on their way through to the States. We put the children up, and fed them, of course. You know, this house is like a transit camp at times. Anyhow, the children stayed here and one day we had tinned pineapple. It came out of the tin in whole slices, and one of them complained, "We only eat pineapple in cubes." I remember wagging my finger at him and saying prophetically, "You will get used to eating whole slices, even whole slices of pineapple!"'

Walter Levi enjoyed telling his story and looked round for approval. The children poked at their food, so, particularly for them, he repeated emphatically, 'You, too, will have to get used to eating whole slices of pineapple.'

Hannah spoke up. 'Daddy is a black marketeer and he exploits the workers.'

Fräulein von Seydlitz was indignant. 'Hannah, how can you say such a thing? How can you? Your father works hard and he makes sure that you have decent food. What is wrong with that?'

If Walter Levi was annoyed by his daughter's attack, he did not show it.

'The younger generation is so idealistic. I think it is in school that they acquire such high moral standards; the belief that everything should be shared out equally. I did not see you refuse your egg this morning, Hannah, and that came from deepest Acton. I gave a tin of peaches for the half-dozen eggs.'

He explained to Karl and Margot. 'That is where my factory is. Yes, we too help with the war effort, we make floor polish. Not frightfully good polish, what can one do? The decent ingredients are just not available. But the stuff smells of pine essence, it spreads quite well and the neurotic housewife, who has a great urge to scrub and clean, can do so. Then she feels better and so we help to maintain morale. There is nothing else

57

in the shops, people are desperate to spend their money and so our polish sells very nicely. And it is not easy,' he looked at Hannah, 'to run a good factory these days. You should see the people we have to employ. The majority are women, and their husbands are more likely in prison than in His Majesty's Forces. We can't get them to come regularly. They are not interested in overtime, they just stay away when it suits them. Sometimes that has advantages; the other day the factory inspector called. When everyone turns up for work there are not the statutory number of lavatories. But we were lucky; there were so many absentees we passed – please excuse such an indelicate topic at lunch.'

Karl was enjoying the custard which was creamy and not a bit like the yellow mixture he was given at school; and the apricots were juicy. He felt as if he had not eaten anything as good for a long time.

'Who is going to help with the washing up?'

Karl could tell from the tone of Frauelein von Seydlitz's voice that washing up was a frequent source of irritation and conflict. He volunteered but she said, 'Oh, not you, you are a guest, it's one of these lazy ones I want to help.'

In the end it was he and Fred who went out into the kitchen to clean up while Hannah watched. Karl wanted to make a good impression. In any case washing up and drying were not things he usually did and he quite enjoyed the domestic activity. By Karl's standards the kitchen was luxurious. He looked into the fridge and there was a huge bowl of egg and mayonnaise sandwich spread. Hannah explained.

'We put that on sandwiches when we feel like it. I suppose that is one advantage over being in a boarding school. At least you can eat when you feel like it. Mind you, sometimes I wonder if I am all that lucky being at home.'

She teased Frauelein von Seydlitz. 'It makes *you* happy having me here, doesn't it?'

Frauelein von Seydlitz replied sourly, 'Oh yes, you make my life one round of pleasure. Come on, you help with the drying, the boys are doing all the work while madam graciously makes polite conversation.'

As the Frauelein went out of the kitchen Hannah burst out, 'Stupid Prussian cow' – Hannah spoke in English – 'always on at me. She can't bear to leave me in peace. Nag, nag, nag. I just don't know why we need her here. She is pedantic, obsessional and everything has to be just right. Do you know she has a special little cloth for the dining room table. She and Dad are mad about that table, it must not get scratched. One day, she came in, really furious and snapped, "Behind my back someone has been using my special cloth to wipe up with, and without my permission." We were in hysterics, rolling on the floor with laughter, and, of course, she has no sense of humour. She looked quite puzzled. Then she went and reported us to Dad and there was a fuss.'

Karl noticed how different Hannah was when there was no adult in the room. She became animated and full of laughter.

'I bet you like it here? Do you want to come and stay here for your holidays? I don't see why not, everyone else seems to stay here.'

Karl was embarrassed. This was far too direct for him. He *had* thought to himself that it was an exceedingly comfortable house and anything would be better than the Hodge sheets. Then there was the bowl of egg sandwich spread in the fridge. He had thought how nice it would be to dip into it every time he felt a bit hungry. That would be just like it had been at home. At school they were always scavenging for food – extra bread from the kitchen for toast in the study and if they were lucky some dripping. Best of all, if he was in time, the bit of meat essence at the bottom of the dripping. But usually the more senior prefects got there first. Then Karl remembered bitterly how it always seemed to be he who was sent by Douglas to go down to get bread and dripping. 'Go on,' he would say, 'you with your foreign charm, see if you can get a bit extra, and perhaps you can do yourself some good with Betty.' Betty was the voluptuous kitchen maid. Karl's mouth went all dry and he would blush and stutter when he tried to talk to her. She just smiled and handed over the tray with the bread on it. As she leant forward he could see down the front of her dress and his knees went all weak.

Anyhow, Hannah obviously liked him enough to think he might come to them for the holidays, or at any rate she did not object. 'Everyone else seems to stay' was not exactly what Karl would call a hearty offer of hospitality but it wasn't unwelcoming, either.

Walter Levi appeared at the kitchen door, 'I do appreciate that you have helped with the washing up. We are going for a little walk. You will come, won't you?'

With Walter Levi Karl had a suspicion all the time that he was being directed in the way Walter wanted to go, but it was done with such beautiful delicacy that he was hardly aware of Walter's authority. Walter put on a stiff, black hat with a silk ribbon round the brim.

'My city hat,' he said. 'When I got to England I looked round to see what people were wearing. The right clothes are so important. What impact can you have in a business discussion if you are not wearing the right clothes? Mind you, I have always worn English clothes, there is nothing like them. Before the war, whenever I was in London, I would see my tailor, and of course he had kept my measurements and I just ordered a suit. Extraordinary, there I was with my city hat on and I met Perl, of the big financial group, although his father created that. He was and is a fool. When he saw me he sneered, "Ah, Walter, the right hat, you *would* have the right hat straight away." I thought, you may sneer but who is getting the business contacts?'

Karl thought about his own shabby suit that was short at the sleeves. One good thing about wartime was that no one seemed to take much notice at school whether your clothes were new or not. Karl did, though. He was very conscious of the suits of some of the boys. John's grey suit was a much better cloth than anyone else's, and he had noticed Walter's cashmere pullover as soon as he opened the door. Now he had a coat on and a beautiful silk scarf round his neck.

'We are going to see my mother. She has a flat not far from here and she will be so pleased to see you. She has heard so much about you from my sister. You seem to be getting on well with the children.'

Karl thought of his inconclusive conversation with Fred, but wanted to make it sound as if they had already struck up a wonderful friendship.

'Yes, Fred and I are studying the same period in history,' he said.

'He has not been happy lately. I am sure friendship with you, someone his own age, will cheer him up, and you are so good at making contact with people. I wish he had that gift. Now Hannah, she will talk to anyone, but poor Fred, I am sure you are a good influence. I thought I noticed him cheer up.'

Karl felt an utter fraud. He had done nothing and it seemed to him nothing had happened, but he resolved to make friends with Fred; that was expected from him. As it was he was walking with Hannah.

'I hate Sunday afternoons. The visit to dear Grandmother. You have got a treat coming to you. Well, you are 'family' and she will be gracious. She is vicious really, absolutely vicious and she hates me. I can't do anything right. I wish a bomb had dropped on her. Now Fred, he is her darling. Just watch what happens when we get there. I will be ignored or, if I am lucky, told off. But poor Fred! She puts his head on her lap and strokes him. I said to her, "How about buying a cat if you must stroke something," and got told off for being cheeky. Everyone is scared of her except me. Dad humours her and she makes her lady companion cringe. Watch Frau Cohn when we get there. She sticks her behind outwards and waggles like a dog and cringes, "Yes, Frau Geheimrat, no Frau Geheimrat." Creep, creep – they make me sick.'

The door to the flat was opened by Frau Cohn. Karl just stopped himself from laughing. Hannah had been absolutely accurate. Her bottom stuck out and she seemed to be dancing round Walter.

'Frau Geheimrat has had a very good night, she is so very much looking forward to seeing you. She has been asking me every ten minutes to go to the window to see if you were coming. These are the Hartlands? I am so pleased to meet you and Frau Geheimrat is looking forward to seeing you. This way.'

She ushered them into the presence. The flat smelt exactly like his own grandmother's, the one he had not liked very much and who had hated him for being a boy. The smell was probably the polish, beeswax. Karl commented on the smell to Walter who laughed.

'One thing you can be sure of, it isn't the polish we make in our factory. Here you are, Mother, this is Karl, the Hartland boy, Max Hartland's boy. You remember I told you we were all coming to see you this afternoon. What's all this about worrying over us? I told you we were going to be in time for a nice cup of coffee.'

The old lady sat in a corner, very upright, a shawl draped round her shoulders. She had a fresh pink complexion and very dark, coalblack eyes. Her hair was wonderfully arranged and nothing was out of place. In her time, Karl thought, she must have been a beautiful woman. A walking stick with an ivory handle was leaning against her chair. Her voice sounded as if she had been through some sort of private agony.

'I have been waiting for ages. I slept so badly last night.'

Walter exchanged looks with Frau Cohn, who stood at a respectful distance and shrugged her shoulders as if to say 'nonsense'. Walter teased gently.

'I know what it is, Mother, you want more of your medicine.' And to the others, 'We keep a bottle of very good brandy for medicinal purposes in the bathroom cupboard and it has helped Mother through the air raids, a wonderful tonic.'

She turned to Karl, delighted that he was teasing her.

'He is awful but he is a good son, a wonderful son. Has it been a hard week? I think it is wonderful the way he has adjusted to the new life, the factory. If you knew the sort of people he has to deal with. Things have changed.' Then she seemed to remember that she had not met Karl before. 'So you are Karl, Max Hartland's boy. I have heard about you, and the children have looked forward to meeting you.'

Karl saw Hannah rolling her eyes upwards. It was as if there were a secret conspiracy between them. Walter Levi explained.

'He goes to a boarding school, and I have just seen his report

62

this morning. He is doing very well. And Margot is winning the war for us, making vital aeroplanes in Cricklewood.'

Old Mrs Levi sighed. 'Everyone is doing war work these days. Do you know they even wanted to call up Mrs Cohn, and she is my housekeeper. What would I do without her?'

Mrs Cohn glowed at such praise. 'Really, Frau Geheimrat, it is nice of you to think so well of my work. I'll get the tea.'

As she went out of the room Mrs Levi said, 'I suppose that pleased her, she is such a *nebbich*.' Then to Karl, 'You know what a *nebbich* is?'

'Yes, someone whom you feel sorry for.'

Walter Levi asked everyone. 'Did you hear of the poor old Jew. They asked him what he wanted most and he said, "If I could only say, *that* Hitler, *nebbich*." I am glad you haven't forgotten everything.'

Karl said that he felt odd speaking German all the time. He really had not forgotten everything, but to underline that he was now well on the way to becoming an Englishman, he wanted to make it clear that English had become his first language, so he pretended to search for a word more than he needed to. All in all he preferred to talk in German, the English of the older Levis was almost unbearable. Sometimes they would break into English for a sentence or two. At one point Mrs Levi asked in English, 'And what did you have for loench?'

'Not loench, lunch,' Hannah corrected.

'I learned "loench", and I had my own tutor, a very nice young lady from a good family. I was assured that she did not speak "Cockney", and if she said it that way I am sure it was right. I wish you would not criticize the way I talk.'

Hannah persisted. 'But it is lunch *not* loench – I ought to know, I go to an English school, don't I?'

Grandmother Levi completely ignored her and turned to Fred. 'My dear boy, how are you today? Come to Oma, you look tired. The poor boy has been working too hard. Come, put your head on my lap.'

Fred put his head on her lap and she stroked it, murmuring 'poor boy' and ignoring everyone else. Hannah gave Karl a triumphant look and he wanted to giggle. It was like being in prayers at school, where some sort of good behaviour was expected but there was a sort of subterranean resistance movement. In school hymn books were battered down on any boy misbehaving; it did not hurt much though it made a huge noise. Karl expected a hymn book to come down on him now. Every time he looked at Hannah he wanted to giggle, but he remembered about making a good impression. When he had first walked into the room he had noticed a huge portrait, and had read the name 'Lieberman' in passing. He knew that Lieberman was a German painter, an impressionist because he had seen his paintings in the house of the 'other' Hartlands. All Lieberman paintings had been removed from the Essen art gallery because he was a Jew. So he asked, 'Is that a Lieberman over there?'

The painting was far enough away to make it impossible for Karl to have read the signature at that distance. Walter was pleased.

'Ah you know Lieberman. Yes, that is a portrait of my father. Lieberman was a friend of the family's and often ate with us. My father, yes, a remarkable man. Do you think the portrait conveys his greatness? I told my mother she could have it in her flat. It means so much to her and it is so like him.'

Karl looked at the painting. A remarkably ugly, bad-tempered looking, little man stared at him. Glaring, malevolent eyes, he thought. He noticed a red and white ribbon on his chest.

Walter Levi said, 'The order of the Imperial Eagle, awarded by His Imperial Majesty, Wilhelm the Second – quite honestly, I think he paid for it. One could get honours by paying for them – like the title Geheimrat – that meant absolutely nothing except to the poor arriviste German Jews who could then pretend they were members of the German aristocracy. It was like the Iron Cross second class. By the end of the last war they said the crosses were issued with the rations.'

Walter was a wonderful story teller. To the rest of the family the stories were obviously old hat and boring and they sat there with glazed looks in their eyes, except for Frau Geheimrat who looked adoringly at her son, stroking her grandson's head at the same time. She nodded in agreement when Walter went on telling them of his father.

'He came from Silesia, a tiny dump no one has ever heard of. He arrived in Berlin with a small suitcase to make his fortune and became a cashier at a bank, Lafayette and Kornhauser, near the Imperial Palace. When you come to our house next time,' – (Karl was pleased to hear the 'next time') – 'I will show you an eighteenth century print of the square. It is a charming little print. Father worked really hard and before long he knew much more about the business than his employers. They had become lazy, with aristocratic pretensions and full of snobbery; great anti-semites as well. All the German upper crust were; but it was what we called "salon anti-semitism", just a social sort of exclusiveness. There were certain clubs Jews could not belong to, certain regiments – like the guards – where no Jew could get a commission. Well, my father knew all about the business and customers valued him, trusted him, and he made money on his own. And so one day he went to see old Lafayette (I knew him when I was a little boy), and said, "Please, Mr Lafayette, I want to become a director of the Bank." Well, old Lafayette, a real old Prussian if ever there was one croaked at my father, "What do you mean? A directorship?" It must have taken real *chuzpah* not to run out of the room. My father went on, "Either you take me in or I set up a bank of my own and I'll take your most important customers with me." Now that was a genuine threat and they knew it, so they let him become a director. And then my father said, "I want some shares, too." At that the old man exploded, "What, you mean to say you have got money as well?" Eventually my father took the whole bank over, bought out the old owners. They never liked him much, but they could not stop this upstart from Silesia. When my poor father died he handed over the whole thing to me. My brother had died in the war – he was killed, but that is another story.'

Grandmother Levi nodded approvingly, 'Yes, a remarkable man. He started with nothing and made his own way.'

Walter Levi continued, 'He fell in love with my mother at a health resort, Baden Baden.'

Hannah chipped in, 'Wasn't her mother a boarding house keeper?'

'Yes, like my father her family started with very little, not like some spoilt brats round here who take everything for granted.'

Hannah was cross, 'Well, you inherited the lot, didn't you? You did not have to start as a bank clerk.'

Grandmother Levi was very angry but it hardly showed. Her black eyes seemed to sparkle a bit more and her cheeks were a shade more pink. 'I wish you could be more polite to your father. He took on enormous responsibilities when he was only a very young man, and he was a great success in Berlin. Everyone knew your father. People used to say, "there goes young Levi." And you don't live too badly here, you know.'

'Yes,' Walter Levi took up her last remark, 'I noticed when things were getting hot; I wasn't going to wait once they began to inspect my books and ask awkward questions. Do you know, it became an offence to have foreign currency? I knew it was time to go. I hated to go, we had had a good life in Berlin, but I could read the danger signals.'

Karl wished his own father had read the danger signals early enough. He found it difficult to understand why his father had not come to England, or just left Germany for that matter. Then he would not have had to put Karl on a train with a label round his neck. Perhaps they would not have been able to live in the Levi style, but he imagined they would have been quite comfortable. He would not have had to sleep in Mrs Hodge's basement. He might even have had milk with his supper at school, and his suit might have been a better quality. Why had his father stayed behind? He had talked to Margot about it, but she was not quite sure either.

'I think he could not bear to emigrate with very little money and be a nobody, perhaps having to clean shoes in a hotel as some refugees do. Also, I think it had something to do with Mutti's death. He just did not care all that much. As long as he got us two to safety he could not be bothered to save himself. Then there was his responsibility to the Jewish community – after all, when Uncle Arnold went to the States he became the head of the community, and he may have felt that he had a responsibility there. It's almost impossible to understand his motives.'

66

Karl was angry with his father, and yet would he have wanted to live like this? He felt like an outsider watching the activities of a very complex tribe. As if he was standing behind an invisible curtain he could not get through. The Levis amused and repelled him. He felt envious of Fred, who had his hair stroked gently by the sinister grandmother, but he was more on Hannah's side – Hannah, who tried to survive by attacking them all.

Walter Levi was still reminiscing about his father. 'He became a town councillor. In Berlin that was an important office and I believe he got the decoration for his activities there.' He laughed, 'I'll tell you how he made a lot of money. You will never guess. Cemeteries – yes, don't look so puzzled. Think, you divide a large plot of land into very small pieces and sell each piece at a great price to the grieving relatives. They don't bargain, they are too upset. So a vast profit can be made.'

The grandmother was still stroking Fred. She smiled adoringly at her son. She had enjoyed the stories about Berlin. 'Walter, how are things at work?'

She turned to Karl and Margot and explained, 'He works so hard, he goes every day and really takes his coat off and gets down to it. It's such a marvellous success. He is not like so many of the other refugees who just sit and moan.'

Walter Levi answered his mother's question.

'The factory. Yes, we are not doing badly, it's going well. We are thinking of diversifying. The floor polish market must come to an end. Everyone buys one tin of polish but never another one. We are thinking of dolls. There is a great shortage of toys in wartime. The toy factories are mainly making war materials, and if we can get the materials we need we might do just that. We have this genius, a real genius, with us and he thinks the stuff we use for the polish could, with a few additions be made into material for dolls.'

Karl suggested that perhaps the dolls could be used for polishing floors once the children had broken them. Walter was amused. 'Hah, a sense of humour, good. Yes, that's a good idea; perhaps you will join us in the factory. We need people with good ideas.'

He turned to his mother. 'Guess who called in, Mutti? Gerson, no, not the furniture Gerson. The one who had that small bank. He has been doing badly. He was a *nebbich* in Berlin and now he is a *nebbich* in London! An amusing man, though. He started his refugee career as a waiter in a Lyons' Corner House. I think without Lyons the majority of refugees in London would have starved. Well, he was working there and one day someone who had known him in Berlin came in and ordered a cup of coffee. Then he tipped Gerson sixpence. And what did Gerson do? He handed him back the sixpence and said, "You need it more. Get yourself a haircut." Get yourself a haircut.'

Walter Levi was fond of repeating the punchline of a story he was telling. 'And then, Mutti, the Perls; I have told you about them. Do you remember them? She started off working as a manicurist in the Cumberland – I suspect she did more for her clients than manicure nails. Perl stayed at home and did the housework. I remember seeing him with an apron on, feather duster in hand as he opened the door for me, and he said, "Walter, for twenty years I have been supporting her, now it's her turn." Well, why not, but it must have been hard for him. Mutti, he is doing well now, has got a small factory, making coats and belts for the army, a good government contract, making a lot of money. It is interesting, but it seems to me that the people who were successful at home are also working their way up here.' He looked at his watch. 'Mutti, we must go, I'll walk the Hartlands to the tube. It is time for your evening rest.'

His mother sounded petulant. 'You have only just come and you're on your way already. Well, take good care of yourself. Don't go to bed too late.'

The children were on their feet and Hannah had already rushed to get her coat. Mrs Cohn saw them out, whispering to Walter Levi, 'She is not sleeping very well at the moment. Do you think I should mention it to Dr Herz when he calls in the morning?'

As they walked towards the tube station Walter Levi pointed up to the flat. 'Look at the curtain twitching, she is watching us go. Karl will you walk with me?' His tone was grave; Karl was sure that Walter wanted to impress him with the seriousness of what he was about to say.

'I am very pleased that you got on so well with the children. Did you, perhaps, wonder where their mother was?'

Karl had indeed wondered, but had also decided it would not be good manners to ask.

'My wife left me last year and we are divorced. It has been a difficult time for all of us and, not surprisingly, the children are a bit upset. Not Hannah so much, she is the tough one, she sees her way through anything. No, it is Fred I worry about. He is so quiet and depressed. Did you see him with my mother? She is the only one who seems to have a deep relationship with him. What did you think of Fred?'

Karl was flattered that his opinion was being asked about someone who was more or less his own age.

'He seemed depressed and not happy. He told me he had a new bike but he did not seem very pleased about it. I got the impression that nothing pleased him very much.'

'There you are, you have hit the nail on the head. That's what Loewenberg said. He is my psychiatrist, perhaps you have heard of him?'

No, Karl had not heard of him but he thought to himself, 'I could be a psychiatrist. It can't be all that difficult if I can come to the same conclusion about Fred without any training.'

Walter Levi was still talking. 'When things went wrong I went to him for a consultation, and of course he told me some home truths. He is a first class man, and I was staggered by his deep insights. We discussed Magda, of course. Magda is my wife's name. He said to me, "What is happening is that she is experiencing a late adolescent revolt." I had shown him some of the poetry she had been writing. Poetry! I always thought it rubbish and had told her so. Do you know what Loewenberg called it? "The slime of puberty," yes, "The slime of puberty" – something she ought to have got rid of in some other way. Of course it was not all her fault . . .'

Walter Levi was talking almost feverishly; when he stopped he looked at Karl significantly and pointed his finger to his forehead. '. . . the whole family – *meschugge*. It runs in the blood. They are all odd. You should meet her brother. He is like a wet rag. No will of his own, and that dreadful wife of his. Loewenberg wondered whether there was not some sort of peculiar relationship between her and Magda. But the brother, do you know he wanted to be a toolmaker, yes a toolmaker. He is quite happy now that he has emigrated – he works in a factory and makes tools. Extraordinary. He has become a proletarian, wears an overall and works at a bench. No wonder things were not quite normal with us, either.'

They had reached the tube station, 'It has been a real pleasure meeting you both. I am sure we will see more of each other.'

In the tube Margot sounded excited. 'The poor man, he has suffered a great deal, did you see that melancholy look in his eyes. There he is, on his own, and he has to look after the children. He got custody, so the blame must have been hers. What a lovely house, even their own air raid shelter. That's what I call classy, not having to mix with the masses. You were lovely baby brother, you behaved beautifully. You can be really charming when you try. Ah well, they say good breeding shows even in adversity.'

Karl thought about the hair combing and the 'baby brother' stuff. He wanted to get back at Margot, and decided on a psychoanalytic form of attack because he thought he might do it rather well. In any case, it was time he got into training for his new psychoanalytical approach to life.

'You rather go for elderly gentlemen, don't you? It must be something to do with the unresolved oedipal struggles of your youth. Why don't you try to get to know Mr Levi better? He's got a lovely house, ready made cheerful children, and Frauelein von Seydlitz thrown in as an extra.'

Margot was furious. 'You are a tiresome adolescent and I wish you would keep your half-baked opinions to yourself,' she shouted.

Karl was a bit surprised that she was reacting so strongly, but he was also pleased to have hit home. Yes, he was certainly discovering a talent for analysis in himself.

'Here you are laying down the law and what have you spent all the holidays doing? Nothing,' she went on.

That made Karl cross. Admittedly he had not read as much as he might have done, but he had spent hours in the library.

Margot's mood changed. 'Oh, never mind, baby brother. I am sorry. Anyhow, what we must do next is get you some new things. We'll go to the Woburn House as Alice suggested and see if you can be given a new suit, and perhaps even shoes. That's what you need most.'

Karl burned with shame. To be given charity clothes. He was so humiliated that it did not even occur to him that his sister might find having to ask for charity equally repulsive.

They were given a voucher for a suit, and a pair of shoes which, luckily, were new. The suit turned out to be a good one. Karl had been afraid the clothes would be like the farm uniform he had had issued to him at the approved school; corduroy breeches, a brown jacket, all smelling of grease and poverty. This suit was a completely normal one.

'Nice bit of suiting,' teased Paul, fingering the cloth rather like Karl's old uncle Julius who had been in the cloth business.

'Nice bit of *schmatter*. Yes, very good.'

Paul, who was a very good mimic, sounded like a mixture of Shylock and a salesman. He asked Karl, 'Good hols?'

'Oh yes, good hols.' Karl felt he could not mention the disgusting basement with the nice Mrs Hodge; or that strange family. He felt he had looked into a murky pool. Part of him had wished he belonged to that comfortable arrangement, but more of him had felt repelled. He and his relations could not do without each other, but when they were together they did not make each other happy. Karl, for Paul's benefit, wanted to make the issue more abstract.

'It does seem to me,' he said, 'that living in a family is a strange and dangerous business. How can one stay sane in a family?'

71

Chapter 4

'He's killed a bloke – a soldier.' Ben was so excited his voice was squeaky.

'Who killed a soldier, for Christsake?' Karl was so desperately curious, he even said 'Christsake', although Paul had told him off about that. Anyhow, with Ben it was all right. Even if officially Greek Orthodox (and Karl secretly thought that was one of Ben's fantasies), Karl saw him as a fellow heathen and Jew.

'It's Barnes. He was on duty with the Home Guard last night and he shot a Canadian in a pub.'

'But how could he? Did they have a fight?'

'No. It appears the Home Guard was called in to stop a riot or a fight of some sort. Barnes turned up with his men. Can you imagine him in charge of anything?'

Karl couldn't. Barnes was a huge man with a walrus moustache and thick, square, stubby fingers, dark brown with tobacco stain. When he taught them German he always wore the same smelly green coat. Instead of a tie he wore a thin red piece of something that might have been handknitted. Not that life was easy for Barnes; he had to teach Karl German, and although Karl pretended to search for words when he was with other refugees in London, it had not taken him long to realize that Mr Barnes' German was, to say the least, inadequate. Both he and Ben delighted in correcting his mistakes, and arguing fiercely over any literary judgement Barnes might make during endless boring afternoons, working their way through their set books. The only saving grace Barnes had was that he could be distracted. Possibly for him anything was better than to be corrected, nagged and ridiculed by these two refugee boys. He had a bad enough time in ordinary school where he found it very difficult to control even the youngest boys. Barnes, as he told Ben and Karl several times, had not been called up, firstly because he had a 'dicky heart', and secondly because his political convictions only made it possible for him to join the war effort when Hitler attacked Russia. That was how he came to be in the Home Guard. The boys nearly fell on the floor laughing when they saw him in uniform. His belly was so enormous that the jacket would not close over it, and his trousers did not come together either, so there was a huge diamond in front where his khaki shirt showed. Karl, however, noticed the pip on each shoulder and was impressed. He wished he too could be an officer and useful.

Now Ben was telling him that Barnes had shot a Canadian. When their next period of German came he did not turn up.

'I bet he is too upset,' said Ben. 'What a pity! We would have had a lovely period of revelations: "How I won the war single-handed, wiping out the Canadian forces".'

'Are you sure it happened? I mean you might have imagined the whole thing in your fevered brain . . .'

'No, honestly, I heard it this morning. He told this man to stop fighting but instead he went for him, and then Barnes shot him. I wonder what will happen to him. He should be shot himself, if not for killing the Canadian, for boring us to death slowly.'

Karl was more shocked than Ben who managed to appear coolly supercilious and enjoyed speculating on the outcome of the incident.

'I daresay he will be charged with manslaughter. Or, as he must have been in some danger, there is just a chance he might get away with justifiable homicide.'

'But the Canadians are our allies. What right has he to shoot one of their men?'

'But you know how wild those Canadians are. What chance has Barnes of controlling them if he can't even control the first years. I would have shot a man who was coming at me. If it is either him or me, well then it has to be him.'

Later in the week Barnes was back. He tried to appear casual but his hand shook slightly as he stuffed tobacco into his short, foul pipe.

'Yes, there was an enquiry, a post-mortem, and they said I had been acting in self defence and I had been doing my duty. So that's that; if you don't mind we will now get on with reading *Joan of Arc*.'

Obviously Barnes did not want to say any more, but Karl kept on thinking about the man's death and what had happened. Death was in evidence all round them. Every day there was news of bombing raids. Vanessa, Steve's wife, commented sharply, 'I was in a bus the other day, sitting behind a couple of young men. They were in the Air Force. I am sure they were air crew, they had those little badges on their chests' – (Karl was disgusted. 'Little badges' indeed – they were either pilots, bomb-aimers or gunners. Vanessa's vague description saddened him because it meant that she did not care very greatly what these men did.) 'They were handsome, clean-cut young men, who must have belonged to some religious sect. They were talking about who was coming to one of their meetings, and of feelings of fellowship in Christ. It made me quite ill. These beautiful men, full of religious conviction, believing in Christ's love of man, and at the same time dropping bombs on men, women and children. They seemed quite unable to connect their humanitarian, love-thy-neighbour religion with their actions. They drop their destructive bomb loads and then go off to a religious meeting, cleansing each other's souls. Yes, Karl, you look shocked, I know this war was forced on us, but at least let us be honest about what we are doing. God is always invoked by both sides in a conflict, but wasn't it Napoleon who said "God is on the side of the big battalions". I can't stand the hypocrisy of young men like that. They should be clear about what they are doing and accept responsibility for their actions. I expect they would argue that it is God's will, and that they are on the side of "goodness and light". I can't stand the awful waste of life, and the brutality of war.'

'Did you know Turner was dead?'

Karl knew Turner, the terrible Turner, whom Steve had expelled because he had come into the playground with his cigarette alight, his tie hanging to one side and no cap. He had become an air gunner and had visited the school once. The boys had crowded round him.

'What's it like in the Air Force?'

And he had replied nonchalantly, 'All right. Once you pass all the courses and get to be air crew it's a good life. Bloody marvellous, in fact. Do you know, every time you go on ops you get bacon and eggs!'

He had been to Canada to train, and on his chest was half a wing with AG embroidered in the middle of the loop. He seemed to stick his chest out a bit when he talked about his training. Karl had decided he was going to be an air gunner if they would ever take him.

Turner said, 'The average life of an air gunner is ten minutes in action. Once you are stuck at the back of a Lancaster, that's it. Arse-end Charlies, they call us.'

Karl was enthralled. Ten minutes and that was it. What would they say about his death in school? Would it be the 'dulce et decorum' bit? He noticed that both the Gymnasium, his old school in Essen and the Grammar School at Elmfield had the same inscription on their war memorial. Steve had already announced the death of several old boys in prayers. It was obvious that he was upset.

'Better than in the first World War,' the geography master told them. 'Do you know, my old headmaster broke down and wept. There were so many names that as he read them out he sobbed. No, the casualties are nothing compared with the last time.'

Would they weep for him, Karl wondered. He hoped that someone would. Death would not seem all that bad, if the English had accepted him and thought he had repaid them for their kindness in offering him safety. Would it not be the least he could do? He felt another emotion; the sheer dread that he might die without ever having slept with a girl. 'No,' he thought, 'that's got nothing to do with it. I wouldn't mind getting killed. Who wants to go on and on. Look at the slow decay of the old, their sagging skin, how slowly they move. They can't be really happy – it would be best to go out in a cloud of glory.'

Paul was irritated when Karl told him all this. 'You silly sod. A cloud of glory? Rubbish, it's just a disgusting, messy business. I intend to survive, and if I can get a quiet clerk's job in a ministry, that's all I intend to contribute to this glorious war.'

Ben, of course, analysed.

'It's the death wish. Read Freud on the discontents of our civilization. We are tearing ourselves apart. It's all because of sexual frustration and the inability to come to terms with life. Anyhow, you've got to overcome your tendency to daydream and be realistic. They want you to feel the way you do; it's their idea, play on our idealism and get us ready to be killed.'

'But don't you detest Fascism,' Karl asked. 'Don't you think it should be fought?'

'Yes, but I also think of what I can't do. Look, when we meet someone who has actually killed a man, like that slob Barnes, both of us get quite disgusted. You aren't nearly as fierce and brave as you think you are. I watched your face, and you recoiled with disgust when he was so bland about the whole business. It's one thing to have great ideals, another to have to stick a knife into someone.'

Douglas had gone into the army and there was to be a new head of house. When they were told it would be Hugh Phillips, Harry Pring was utterly disgusted.

'I mean to say, what are we coming to? It must be that snoop Steve trying to get his clever sods in.' He looked at Karl meaningfully and went on, 'Hugh used to be one of the lads, great friend of Turner and Stone. Do you know, he was nearly expelled with them? Then suddenly he writes some good essays and off we go. Headmaster's favourite, and now head of house. Christ Almighty! Why doesn't he stay at home? His dad's a grocer, why can't he stay there?'

Karl wondered which was worse, a father who was a grocer or one who was a banker. He rarely admitted that his father had been a banker. People said such stupid things. 'Banker? A capitalist? You must have been rich.' Karl had never thought of his father as rich, although he knew that compared with some of the boys at school he had had good clothes, and that the things in his own home were of fine quality. He did not like Hugh, who was distant and unhelpful. Once Karl had asked him, 'Have you got anything good on the Counter-Reformation? Could I have a look at the essay you wrote for Steve?' and Hugh had said very sharply, 'I had to find out for myself. Why can't you? I don't see why you should crib all my work.'

Harry Pring and John consulted each other after the Head's announcement.

'Tell you what, when he comes dancing into the study tonight we'll de-bag him; that should calm him down a bit. A sodding day-bug must know his place.'

Karl thought, 'If they ever try to take my trousers off I will fight so hard they will give up. I couldn't stand the embarrassment. Still, if we do it to Hugh it will be interesting to see what happens. He is so stuck up and conceited.'

It did not occur to Karl that Hugh was unpopular and isolated because he was unsure of himself, frightened and jealous of the other prefects. Karl was so full of these feelings himself he was incapable of understanding that they could exist in others. Since he lacked Paul and Ben's ability to analyse the motives of others, his uncertainty made him aggressive. He so desperately wanted to be accepted by John and Harry that he not only agreed to the de-bagging but helped to plan it.

'We can get him when he comes in tonight after prep. The juniors will all be in bed, they need not know anything about it. We will have to look out, though. Hugh may be a creep but he is tough.'

'Tough as shit and twice as nasty,' Harry continued. 'Yeah, one to each arm, one to each leg and two sit on him; we'll get him. "It can't be helped it must be done, down with your knickers and out with your bum." Perhaps a bit of ink?'

John was enthusiastic, 'Yeah, ink. Ink his balls in, that's good!'

When Hugh came into the study they all jumped on him. But

to Karl's immense surprise Hugh hardly put up a fight at all. There was just one brief struggle when the table was overturned and books scattered all over the floor.

'Right! Off with his trousers!'

Hugh looked furious but did nothing, though he was obviously seething inwardly. Karl could see that.

'Got the ink? Keep still, Hugh, if you don't struggle your trousers won't get ripped. Can't afford a new pair in the middle of term, can we?'

Philip came into the study at that moment. 'Christ, what are you doing, you stupid sods? Seven against one, Marvellous! Get off him!'

John snarled, 'Fuck off, Philip, or you'll get the same. We are just debagging old Hugh. He likes it, don't you, old chap?' and he patted Hugh on the cheek.

Philip stood back. They got Hugh's trousers off and Karl noticed how tatty and grey his underpants looked, particularly round the edges. Bucko shouted, 'Right boys, now for the ink. Lovely ink for the knackers. Makes your hair grow.'

When they had poured the ink on they carried him to the sink, which was filled with cold water, and dipped his bum into it. Hugh spoke for the first time. He sounded cold and bitter, 'Have you quite finished?'

He picked his pants and trousers up and rushed out of the room. Suddenly it all became embarrassing. John tucked his shirt in again. He was sweating. 'That should teach the stuck up bastard a lesson.'

Paul and Ben went for Karl the next day. 'Marvellous, isn't it? The prefectorial lynch mob strikes again with good old Karl in the vanguard. Oh, yes, full of heroics when it's ten against one.'

Karl felt it would be a bit lame to point out that there had been only seven of them. He tried to defend what they had done, but Paul snapped, 'It's because he is cleverer than you, isn't it? You had to go for him because he is intelligent and sensitive. Don't you know how disturbed he is?'

Ben added, 'That's right. Steve only took him into the house so that he could work in peace. He's very disturbed and shrieks in his sleep. Do you know he shouted so much in the dorm we thought we ought to tell matron. Honestly, Karl, anything goes with you as long as it keeps you on the right side of that crew. You're so desperate to be liked you'd do any bloody thing. Just wait until Steve hears about this exercise in prefectorial responsibility.'

Karl's face was beetroot red. He wished he had not joined in or, even better, stopped it all. Ben and Paul were right and he hated them for being right. They were out for a walk by a meadow and Paul suddenly shouted. 'Tell you what, let's show Karl what it is like to be de-bagged. Let's get him,' and they threw Karl to the ground.

But Karl fought really hard. 'I warn you, if you go on I'll really hurt one of you. Watch out! I'll lash out and hit hard!'

They struggled desperately, and Karl was sure his head had been injured, but he did not care. He was certain of only one thing: they were not going to take his trousers off. Suddenly, they had all had enough and stopped. Paul said in his warm, sympathetic voice, 'We've hurt you, your ear is bleeding. Sorry, Karl.'

'Sorry? Balls!' Karl panted. 'You just wanted to get me and you bloody well couldn't.'

Steve lit his pipe.

'I liked your last essay, Karl.' (Karl noticed that nowadays Steve used his first name, not Hartland) 'I like the way you try to understand how Luther felt. That was a very good phrase, "Luther shouted and ranted, and it was like a small boy whistling in the dark to show that he was not afraid." That's a very good description . . .'

Karl glowed. He was not at all sure any more whether the phrase was his own or whether he had picked it up while he was feverishly looking for material, but what was so good about Steve's praise was that he had given him credit for something. He had assumed that Karl was good enough to have thought of that phrase for himself. Then it dawned on him, Steve was telling him about himself. He was talking about the de-bagging of Hugh, about how Karl was fighting to be accepted, so that he often acted without much thought, because he was afraid. It was not enough just to daydream about dying heroically in mid-air. The reality was that he was lonely and scared and not accepted. Steve was trying to help him to talk about himself without making him feel embarrassed.

'I am very pleased with the way you are developing, Karl. Your progress has been remarkable. Suddenly you have broken through some sort of barrier.'

Suddenly, irrationally, Karl stopped being grateful to Steve and felt angry with him.

'Doesn't the stupid twat realize,' he fumed, 'that not long ago I couldn't understand a word anyone said. "Come into the sixth form and do history," he told me, but he didn't tell me how to write, and most of the time I still don't know what his lessons are all about. It's all right for him, he's the headmaster, he's got lovely modern paintings and everything he wants, *and* the right to tell me I am making progress.'

On reflection Karl realized that his feelings were what Ben had taught him to call 'ambivalent': you could respect, like and perhaps even love someone and at the same time they could make you very angry. He wondered why Steve made him so angry at times. It was not that he had not allowed him to stay in the holidays? No, Karl knew that had been reasonable. It was the way he made him think about himself: about his motives, his point of view, his emotions.

'What you need,' Steve had said, 'is a point of view. You argue well but you stay outside everything. What do you really believe? I suggest that you adopt the British point of view. I am not saying for a moment that the British are ideal, or have not done some awful things in the past. Indeed, there are some deep contradictions in British behaviour, but they do have a valid point of view.'

Karl remembered how he had said that no one did anything except out of self-interest, and Steve had become angry, 'You, Hartland, are a Machiavelli. Nothing but a Machiavelli.'

Karl discovered later that it was possible Steve had not used the word correctly, because Machiavelli was not just advocating self-interest. He wanted people to achieve a detached under-standing of contemporary political practice. Perhaps Steve's own last remark had been Machiavellian. Karl felt a surge of anger. 'When I argued that Loyola was a self-indulgent maso-chist,' he thought, 'he didn't like that either. Why is he using our abstract arguments in a discussion to make personal capital? Harry Pring is right; he *is* a snooper. He is searching me out and trying to change me.'

But all he said was, 'Could you explain what you mean by the British point of view?'

Steve sensed that Karl was upset, but made no attempt to change the nature of the discussion.

'You see, Karl, you are Jewish but you do not believe in their religion. If I understand it right, the family is the found-ation of Jewish corporate life and you have not got a family any more. There is no cohesion left in your life. Do you know, Isaiah Berlin once said to me . . .'

Karl was relieved that Steve had begun to digress. This sort of talk was painful and uncomfortable for him. He did not want Steve to probe, but at the same he knew that it was not done just out of idle curiosity. Steve had seen that he was troubled, that several value systems were tugging at him.

'Do you know, Karl, it's obvious that you are internalizing the value system of this country. You have no idea how auth-oritarian you were when you came here first . . .'

Karl thought, 'Here we go, back to Axford. Nothing is ever forgotten. Steve has no idea how frightened I was, any more than he will ever be able to understand how little I took in of what was going on around me. Yes, I want to be British – or did he say English? Anything is better than being in any way a part of Germany.'

This was the country that had literally saved his life. Terrible stories were coming through from Germany; there were said to be death camps and executions.

Karl talked to Steve about his fears, and Steve said, 'We must be careful. In the First War there were all sorts of stories spread around by our propaganda people: that the Germans had bayonetted babies, made soap out of corpses and so forth. In the end none of it was true. The same thing may be happening this time. They say in wartime the first casualty is truth.'

Karl wanted to believe Steve. While he was relieved that his father was not there all the time telling him to save his money or to wear a hat or tidy up, he did not want anything bad to happen to him, either. It was difficult enough when the Allies bombed Germany.

'Oh, you are from Essen. Isn't that the place they bombed last night? Well, what do you think of that?'

Years ago, when he had still been at his German school Karl had begun to hate it. The others sneered at him and made him feel uncomfortable in all sorts of ways. His revenge had been secret. He had invented a secret word – a word like the secret name for god in the Jewish religion which no one, but no one, should ever speak. When he touched a place or a wall he would say the word, and then he would persuade himself that the place would blow up. On that basis, the entire weight of the thousand-bomber raids in Essen would have fallen on his old school, the town hall (where they had snapped at him because he kept his stupid hat on) and the police station where they had taken his finger prints. After the raids Karl was a bit frightened that his magic had worked too well.

When Steve talked about magic one day, Karl understood something else about himself.

'Magic is a sort of solution, the dream copes with the un-attainable. So Eskimos dream of kayaks that move effortlessly through the water, the schoolboy lies on his back and dreams of the century he will score at cricket, and . . .' Karl completed the thought for himself, '. . . If I have aggressive feelings I can't contain, if I hate but have not the power to destroy, I resort to the magic of the daydream.'

Yes, the British point of view; it would be good to belong. If only it were easier. But there was pressure from all sides.

'Listen to the little gentleman,' Alice had sneered in London. 'What marvellous pronunciation. You can hardly tell, if at all, that he is a refugee. Before long he won't want to know any of us, he will be far too posh.'

And then there was the pressure from the other side, the

82

school staff. Ben had said ruefully, 'They don't like us, you know, the teachers. Some of them hate us. Not the decent ones, but the ones who hate Steve. Do you remember the major?'

Karl remembered the major, all right. There had been a dreadful scene when the major had accused them of sneering at the cadets. As it happened at that particular moment they had not been sneering at the cadets, although it was true, they did despise them. They looked so odd, those small boys with huge hats and rifles that were too big for them. There seemed to be so much barking at them, too, when they were on parade. But then the major had taken the whole thing personally. He hit Ben across the face during a gym lesson, and accused Karl of cheating during one of the races. As Karl said at the time. 'If I knew how to cheat during a mile race, perhaps I might, but it never occurred to me. It is just that that gruesome Fanny Turner can't bear to lose, and he complained to the major who is his housemaster. Talk about the British being good losers . . .'

'He hates me too,' Ben said sadly. 'Claimed he caught me with my ear to the keyhole in the staffroom, listening to the conversation. Actually, I was looking to see if Stinker was in to give him my essay, but I wasn't listening. Why should I want to listen to their trite drivel? The trouble is they have inferiority complexes. Look at Barnes, all he has ever achieved is the death of one allied soldier. His German would not get him a cup of coffee. And that pathetic Peers dictating notes all the time. Although we had special library work he made us stay in the classroom, then made so much noise we could not get on with it even at the back of the room. That's why they hate us. We're better than they are.'

'Never mind, Ben,' Karl consoled him, 'no one is specially picking on you. We all hate you.'

But Karl knew Ben was right. Some people did dislike the foreign boys; but it was because of their 'foreignness', not because they were Jewish.

'We should attack in the West, now,' Karl had said, and Harry Pring had looked at him and sneered, ' "We"? What do you mean "we"? Why should *you* tell *us* what to do?'

Karl had only blushed then. But now that Steve had suggested he should adopt the British point of view, he felt like shouting, 'You silly bugger. There is nothing I would like to do more than disappear in a cloud of Britishness. All I need is a British accent, British ancestry and a British home. If you can provide me with those, the rest will be easy.'

But it would be unthinkable to say that. He even felt ashamed at letting the idea slip into his mind, for he had far too much respect for Steve.

Steve was still talking about Karl's essay on Luther.

'It is good, you know. What would you say if I put you in for a scholarship at Cambridge? I would not even have considered you six months ago but it seems to me, now, that you are making such great strides . . .'

Karl was amazed and felt terribly guilty for having mentally called Steve a silly bugger who did not understand him. Why, he asked himself, did he find it so difficult to believe that people genuinely wanted to be nice to him. Why did he dwell endlessly on real or imagined slights, mull over every imagined sneer and insult when really this man was on his side, and trying to help. And 'Cambridge'. Surely that must mean that eventually he would belong. The place was only a name to Karl, but even so he had heard a good deal about it.

'In England if you want to belong at all you have to go to either Oxford or Cambridge.' Isobel had told him that. 'They are putting me in for Girton, it's the opportunity of a lifetime. It is not only the snob appeal, but the people you meet. I could be talking to Russell or Ogden – just like that.'

Karl did not know the names but he sensed the excitement. He learned the names of colleges when they were dropped as asides, and he picked them up in the same way he had collected stamps. Now instead of Ruanda Urundi it was 'King's', 'Christ's', and 'Girton'.

'It's a huge Gothic horror,' Isobel told Karl. She was sitting on a wall, waving her legs about. She always wore the same dress, a thin brown one, and a black blazer with the school crest on her pocket. She always made fun of Victorian architecture.

84

'When they were really bombing London, Karl, do you know what we said? "Please, Goering, drop one on the Albert Memorial." But no, that was spared. You must read Lytton Strachey; he is marvellous on the Memorial. Do you know, not a single workman swore while he was working on that building; they all knew they were engaged in a sacred task. I really want to go to Cambridge, and I want Hugh to get in, too.'

Karl felt uncomfortable; the de-bagging incident still rumbled. He had even gone to Hugh and apologized. 'Look I am sorry about what happened . . .'

Hugh had just looked up coldly. 'I bet you are.'

There had been none of that famous sportsmanship, a manly handshake and let bygones be bygones. Karl knew then that Hugh would hate him forever. Isobel had had lessons with Hugh.

'I want Hugh to get in. It will mean so much to the Steves. Steve told me that a few days ago Lady Horton, the wife of the chairman of the governors, came up to him in the street and said in her splendid, screeching voice; "Mr Stevens, I hear that boy from the shop is going to try for Cambridge. Is that a good idea? Is it right? That boy comes from a working class family and he will surely get ideas above his station." I know what I would have said to her; I would have told her about the French Revolution, that all careers should be open to all who have talent. The thought of the guillotine would have advanced her social thinking no end! Surely the Steves want us to get in because they want an open and democratic society.'

Another view of Oxford and Cambridge had been presented to Karl by Gruffyd Edwards, nicknamed Little Ted by the boys. Karl had lived in his house for some time when he first came to the school from the farm camp. Little Ted would sit back, smile happily, and reminisce.

'Yes, I was at Jesus. That's because I am Welsh – lots of Welshmen go there. A beautiful college. We had rules that may seem odd to you. In the evening you wore a black gown and you were not allowed into certain pubs. The university had a sort of private police force, Bullers they were called, and if they thought they saw an undergraduate who was not wearing his gown or was in a forbidden pub they would go up to him and say, "Are you a member of the University?" If you lied and they found out you were sent down. But you could run off – I did once and I gave them a fair run. But the Bullers were picked for running ability and they caught me. The next day I had to pay my fine and that was that.'

Ted's wife, who was less inclined to accept old traditions, said wickedly, 'And do you know, Karl, if they had a lady to tea, they had to push the bed out into the corridor. Indecent I thought it was. The trouble with Gruffyd is that he is an eternal adolescent. He thinks playing games with university porters is what life is all about. Absolute rubbish! And what's more they give you a degree of some sort just for being there. Oxford is for the rich and the idle.'

These comments did not make much impression on Ted, who went rambling on.

'And we had sconcing. If you mentioned the name of a lady at dinner you had to drink a pint of beer and buy one for everyone else; and politics were not allowed either. Nowadays . . .'

When Ted said 'Nowadays' it usually meant he was about to launch an attack on Steve and Vanessa. Ted had liked Steve's predecessor very much, thought him a proper gentleman. All the new things that Steve was introducing, like no beating and a large sixth form upset him.

'Nowadays,' he went on, 'everything is turned upside down. Before long there will be more sixth formers than the rest of the school put together. And who are they doing it for? I think the Steves are just out to make themselves more important. Look at the books they are telling me to get for the library! Rubbish like that Huxley. And she' – meaning Vanessa – 'is mad on Virginia Woolf. Is that supposed to be writing? Now, Karl, read Dickens, a straightforward narrative and no frills. The Bloomsbury set . . .' He went muttering on.

So when Steve said to Karl, 'What would you say if I put you in for a scholarship at Cambridge?' a great number of impressions went through his mind. Most important of all, was, what was it all about? He had such confused views of what a university was. Then he had to ask himself, what were Steve's reasons for putting him up for a scholarship examination? Did it mean Steve thought he was clever? Karl had never thought of himself as clever. He had been hopeless at school in Germany; not entirely hopeless, because they never made him do a year twice over, which was the ultimate disgrace. His sister had often called him stupid, but he might have done better in Germany if he had not hated the school so much. At Elmfield several things had happened to him. Most important of all, he had been treated decently; his opinions were often thought to be interesting even if annoying. Now Steve was talking about Cambridge.

Karl thought of his sister's warning, 'Remember, they don't *have* to pay for you. We must not cost the New York Hartlands too much,' and asked 'Would it cost a lot of money?'

Steve looked irritated and Karl thought, 'God, he thinks I am being mercenary, a small-minded little sod who only thinks in terms of "how much".'

But Steve was not irritated, just thoughtful.

'Yes, the money will be a problem, but it *is* possible to get through university with grants and things like that. What about your family? I am not at all sure who pays for you here. The cheques I get are signed by a Mr Levi. Who is he?'

Karl explained that Walter Levi was acting as agent for his sister, Karl's aunt. She lived in New York, and paid his fees. Walter Levi passed on the money at her request, but was not himself responsible. He knew that the complexities of the family relationships would be too much for Steve, so he merely said, 'The New York Hartlands are cousins.' Steve went on inexorably about money, and Karl wished he would, as usual, get on to another, more abstract less painful, topic.

'I can see money is a problem, Karl. It is obviously something that bothers you, and I can understand you don't want to be indebted to anyone. You see your independence as all important, but independence has to be paid for, and the price asked of you may well be not being too suspicious of other people's motives.'

Karl thought, 'Why shouldn't I be suspicious? I get kicked

out of my own country, I am despised for belonging to a group whose religion I do not believe in and I am pushed from pillar to post. Now, suddenly I am told I am clever and asked if I would I like to go to Cambridge.'

Another thing Karl had learnt was that being clever was not necessarily considered a virtue in England. When people like Harry Pring said, 'clever', they meant 'swot'; when matron called him 'clever', it meant 'cunning little foreign devil, trying to take over our country'; when Little Ted said 'clever', he probably meant 'bloody Bloomsbury set, modern art and rubbish like that.' As for Steve and Vanessa, it was clearly a quality they both admired and desired; but then they were intellectuals, and intellectuals were not that popular either. MaTed, Little Ted's wife, had told Karl with great glee:

'I heard a good story the other day. Lady Horton and her husband, the chairman of the governors, were invited to have tea with Mr and Mrs Stevens. You know how their drawing room is hung with all that modern art; well Lady Horton said to Mr Stevens, "How good of you to hang the boys' paintings in your drawing room. I do like to see the young people's work on display everywhere." That seems to me just about the right comment to make on all that modern stuff they go in for. It's all part of being intellectuals, I suppose.'

MaTed looked very pleased with herself as she recounted the tale, and leant down to fondle their disgusting, slobbering black mongrel. Karl, who thought he liked dogs because he had owned an Alsatian in Germany, hated the beast. She had short, coarse black hair and a peculiar gristly lump on her back.

'Poor Jilly, duckie duddles, we don't know what it is and the doctor doesn't know, but she is a happy duckie duddles, isn't she?' and Jill looked up, muzzle dripping saliva, drooling with adoration.

Karl brought his attention back to Steve again, and thought, 'Yes, Cambridge, and being clever; that's all I've got. Well, I'd better be clever, then, and an intellectual; go in for modern art, Bloomsbury, the lot.' So he said, 'Yes, I would like to try if you think I could manage reasonably well.'

'I think you might make a good impression. We'll try you

for Corpus Christi; a gentlemanly college, but then you are really quite a gentlemanly person.'

Karl was not sure whether Steve was teasing him. Anyhow, it was another name, another college to add to his collection. Steve went on, 'But that won't be till the autumn; late November. First you must think about the holidays. Still a problem?'

Karl had decided to help the war effort in the summer. There had been an appeal for boys to help on farms. If more food was grown in England, it said, less would have to be brought by boat and more space would be left for vital war materials. Karl felt that if they did not want him in the Air Cadets, the Home Guard or the Air Force, he might at least help to bring in the harvest; even more important, he could live on the farm and he would not cost his family anything for the summer. The next Christmas holiday was safe, too. Walter Levi had written to Karl, 'Would you care to spend the Christmas holidays with us? I hope you will not mind sleeping in Fred's room.'

Would he mind! He told Ben about his good fortune. 'They have got a marvellous house. Well, it's mock Tudor; but you should see their paintings.'

Karl slightly exaggerated the importance of the painting collection to make the tale more dramatic. 'There is a Rembrandt, a Guardi and several French Impressionists. When I lunched with them I could not even remind myself that there was a war on. They get food parcels from the States all the time.'

He went on to a rapturous account of the egg sandwich spread in the fridge. 'Every time you feel like it, you go and help yourself.'

Ben asked, 'Is the daughter as available as the sandwich spread? Obviously you must seduce her and then you will inherit all that wealth and you can devote the rest of your life to intellectual pursuits and the arts. Every intellectual should have a private income; it allows for integrity and independence of mind.'

At that moment there was a shattering explosion. Not like

thunder; it was a tighter, even more frightening noise. Both Karl and Ben threw themselves on the floor which seemed to be heaving. When it quietened down they rushed downstairs. Karl was so frightened his legs felt all wobbly and Ben was pale. One of the boys in the playground rushed up to them. He held a jagged piece of metal in his hand.

'Look, it's still hot – we saw him, a German Junkers dropped its load because there was a Spitfire right behind it. It's still hot. It would have torn us to pieces if it had hit us!'

Chapter 5

'Who is coming to the farm?'

Karl wanted to sound jaunty and cheerful. He was hoping to persuade everyone to come, so they would have a marvellous holiday.

'Come on, help to win the war, the good life on the farm. I don't suppose they have any rationing at all on a farm. Bacon and two eggs in the morning, steak and two eggs for lunch. How about it?'

Ben looked singularly uninterested. 'I've got work to do.'

'So have I,' thought Karl, 'but I can't stay here.' He knew that Ben could stay again because he was part of Steve's family. Karl felt envious and attacked Ben. 'Wouldn't do you any harm to do a spot of manual work. Come on, do your little bit.'

Ben looked uneasy. He knew the other boys resented his special relationship with the Steves. 'No, honestly, I must work. The scholarship examination is before Christmas and this is the last chance.'

This made Karl feel anxious, but he turned to Paul. Paul was equally firm. 'Farm work? Don't be silly. Wurzel bashing? What do you think I am?'

'A lazy sod,' Karl mumbled. He already knew how deeply Paul disliked getting any sort of dirt on himself. He avoided games and anything that was at all physical.

'Have you heard of Whistler, the painter? Well, when he was in Paris, he visited some English fellow-artists and they were all doing physical exercises. He looked at them for a while

91

and then said languidly, "I always get my concierge to do that for me".'

Bucko said he would come. 'Yeh, I'll come. My mum's shacked up with a new bloke and he can't stand me, so I'd better find something to do in the holidays. What do you get for an hour's work?'

Karl was disappointed. Bucko did not rate very high on the popularity scales. No one took much notice of him and he was thought to be a joke. The boys had come to realize that all his stories about his glamorous, sex-ridden holidays were fantasy. Karl wanted the great élite, the ablest and the best to come to his farm, and Bucko certainly was not one of the group. But still he told him, 'Sixpence an hour, and I expect they pay overtime. Riding home on the harvest wagon, drinking cider in the fields.' He saw Breughel's harvest festival before his eyes.

Mike said he would come and that pleased Karl. He was fond of Mike who was all right; good at games, a school prefect, liked by everyone, and he made everyone laugh. His only problem was his father because Mike was a day boy and lived at home. Karl and Mike had had a forbidden drink in the Half Moon. There were strict rules about drinking. Karl had no great liking for the warm, flat beer but Mike was reeling.

'Oh god, Karl, I am half pissed already. I can't go home now, my dad will kill me. We are Chapel, you see, and he is dead against drink. Can you smell anything?'

He breathed over Karl's face. Karl asked if belonging to a Chapel also meant belief in pre-destination. Mike was offended.

'Oh shut up! You fucking Germans, you're always intellectualizing. Never mind sodding pre-destination, just because you are doing an essay on Calvin. Just tell me, can you smell the beer?'

At the farm the three boys were received by the farmer's wife, Mrs Oxted. They knew her boy, Kevin, because he came to the school as a day boy. Mike was gloomy about Kevin even before they reached the farm.

'I hate Kevin Oxted. I bashed him over the head with a hymn

book in prayers, because he was chatting. That'll teach him to pay attention to the religious principles that were being advanced. Anyhow I caught him a whacking great crack and he went quite pale. I just hope he's forgotten. He's a sulky little swine.'

Mrs Oxted was hugely shapeless. She wore a cotton dress, and every time she moved everything under it wobbled. Karl saw the likeness to her son, Kevin. The same puffed eyelids and disdainful look. She certainly did not seem very delighted to see the shock brigade that was going to gather in the vital harvest.

'I wasn't expecting you till next week, harvest hasn't started yet.'

Karl was completely deflated by her disparaging manner and thought, 'Where can I go if I can't stay on the farm. This was the date we arranged. Why does she say now that she expected us next week.'

He felt a great hate against this miserable lady, as she waddled ahead of the boys. 'Oh, all right, I'd better show you your room. I expect Mr Oxted will find work for you. I don't think, though, there is much to do.'

She climbed the stairs ahead, up and up into the attic. On the stairs Mike pretended to stick his finger up her behind and they were quite hysterical with suppressed laughter. In the attic there was a huge double bed, and a length of string stretched across the room just below the ceiling.

'You can hang your things on there; wash stand over there. You'll have to get your own water from downstairs. I can't wait on you.'

Karl looked at the bed in horror. One bed for the three of them. Mike was not too impressed either.

'Three of us in there? Are you queer, Karl? Bucko? I'm not sleeping with queers. I always have my doubts about the boarders. Dormitories are dangerous, aren't they? I'm not having my little brown ring snatched by you sods.'

Karl assured Mike that he did not have the least intention of assaulting him.

'Sorry, Mike, but somehow I don't fancy either you or

Bucko. Now MaOxted, that would be nice. What do you make of her?'

Bucko was already hanging his smart shirt on the clothes line.

'That will keep it neat until Saturday. Did you see, there's a dance in the Church Hall? A dance and no school rules.'

They went down the stairs for their tea and there was Mr Oxted. He looked miserable, and certainly not very pleased to see them.

'Harvest hasn't started yet. Can't find much for you to do. Better see the foreman, he might find something. Everything is slow this year.' He gave them a long look. 'So you are from Elmfield. Yes, Kevin told me about you.'

Karl gave an inward groan and looked across to Mike, who seemed unconcerned.

'Yes,' he said calmly, 'played with your Kevin in the Colts. He'll be very good when he's a bit bigger.'

If Mr Oxted was pleased with this compliment he did not show it. They were eating bread, marge and very red jam. Mrs Oxted had already collected their ration books and had made sure all their coupons were in them. She pointed to a framed photo on the wall.

'Our Richard. He's a sergeant. Gunners. He's with the Desert Rats. We haven't seen him for nearly two years.'

Mike muttered under his breath, 'Good luck to him. He's well out of it.'

Kevin came in. 'Look who's here,' he said. 'Come for a bit of a scrounge have you?'

His parents had already left the room and he tore into a piece of bread and jam. 'Don't get the idea that just because you're prefects you're welcome here. This is my home, and you can bloody well shut up.'

Karl prayed to himself.

'You move your head an inch in prayers, you little swine, and I'll bang it so hard your teeth will fall out.'

Later, Mike agreed enthusiastically.

'Yes. Little pin head, I'll flatten it for him, and that'll be doing him a favour.'

94

The next morning old Oxted did not seem to be any happier to see them.

'I suppose you could cut some thistles. Not much to do at the moment.'

Karl screamed inwardly. 'What the hell! I thought we were supposed to be helping the glorious war effort. Here we are, all ready to go, and he doesn't even have any work for us. I bet there won't be any wages, *and* he's not told us how much he is charging for board and lodging.'

The boys were sent to Bert, the foreman.

'You're the scholars, then? The college boys? You don't look as if you were fit for farmwork. Can you tell the difference between thistles and wheat? Well, you can cut some thistles, then. Kevin'll show you the thirty acre field. Here's the sickles. Now don't go busting yourselves, just nice and easy; steady does it when you are not used to it.'

At first Karl enjoyed chopping thistles. He imagined he was cutting off the heads of people he disliked. They worked some distance apart, shouting encouragement and abuse at each other. By the time it was getting dark, though, Karl's fingers were blistered and his arms ached. Still, he told himself, he had at least earned a shilling.

The evening meal was not very jolly. Kevin sat there glowering, old man Oxted just shovelled in his food and mother Oxted waddled to and from the stove bringing them rabbit pie. After that there was apple pie, with hardly any sugar in it, a cup of tea, and then the boys were sent up to bed. They slept badly, banging into each other, and Karl went on cutting thistles in his ragged dreams. In the morning he asked Mike, 'Do you think they'll pay me extra? I cut thistles in my sleep all last night.'

Mike did not even laugh, just moaned about how sore he was, and how he had a blood blister. He said that if this was patriotism, Karl should remember that patriotism was the last refuge of scoundrels.

Bert put them to hoeing. Karl knew all about hoeing. He had done some at the approved school farm camp and it was work he quite liked. He slowly moved down the lines of beet, trying to chop up only the weeds. This was more like real work, he even liked the way his hands were shining as the skin hardened from wielding the hoe handle. He remembered what his mother had once said. 'We have *all* been getting soft, it is time we learned to be tougher.'

She made this remark when the Germans began accusing the Jews of being soft and degenerate, and his father had agreed. 'We must learn to work with our hands again.'

Not that Karl could remember his father ever doing anything with his hands, but the feeling persisted that physical toughness mattered. Steve had explained about the Jews and their role in European history.

'You see, in the Middle Ages they were not allowed to own land. So they were driven into commercial activity; partly because they could not be peasants, but also because the Christians, who did not wish to endanger their salvation by handling money and charging interest, were only too happy to let the Jews do it for them.'

Karl felt good, moving against the heritage of the Middle Ages. He also remembered that if the Christians protected their spiritual welfare by making Jews usurers, the Jews in their turn had protected their own souls by employing *shabbes goyim,* non-Jews who would kindle fires, light lamps and carry heavy things on the Sabbath, all tasks forbidden to the Jew.

Deep in these reflections about the nature of work, Karl was startled by Kevin who had crept up on him.

'Come on, you lazy sod, you are just standing there dreaming. I'm going to tell Father. He's not paying you to stand there half asleep. You may be in the sixth form, but here you work!'

Karl was near to hitting Kevin with the hoe. How dare he say he wasn't working, admittedly at that moment he had been leaning on his hoe, but he had also been thinking about the nature of work and the role of Jews in the Middle Ages.

Later, old man Oxted suddenly appeared out of the hedgerow. Karl was pleased that he was working at the time. No doubt Kevin had made his report, old Oxted looked along the hoed lines but said nothing.

'Trying to find fault, the old bastard,' thought Karl, but the old man said nothing, nodded and disappeared again. Karl was cross.

'He could at least have said, "well done", even if he didn't want to have a discussion on agriculture with me.' But clearly this was not going to be Oxted's style. The day went very slowly. Sometimes it seemed to Karl that the sun was standing still and it would never be evening. He calculated his wages, but they did not come to much at sixpence an hour. The foreman came past once. 'Easy on, son, don't want to bust yourself,' and Karl thought that it was difficult to please everyone in this place.

When he got back to the attic Bucko was packing. His button-down shirts were already in his case, carefully folded.

'I'm off,' he said. 'I'm not staying in this dump. Sod it, I'm not spending all day slaving away and then come back to this shitty dump. I've phoned my mum and it's the next bus for me.'

Karl felt desperate. If Bucko went so might Mike and then he would be all on his own, exposed to Kevin's malice and the general dispirited ill-humour of the Oxted family. He asked, 'How about your wages, you don't get paid until the end. That's what Oxted said.'

'He can stuff my wages up his arse, I'm going.'

Karl did not think that a reminder about the need to grow food to help win the war against Fascism would have any effect on Bucko's decision. He also knew that he would have jumped on the bus with him if there had been any real alternative to staying on the farm. He was relieved when Mike said he wasn't going.

'God no, I'm not going. In the first place there's no one at home, they have gone to my grannie's in Wales and I can't stand the old bag. I'm not leaving yet, there's the harvest to come when we'll make more money, and there's the dance on Saturday. Anyhow, we'll be more comfortable at night now. I couldn't stand sleeping with three of us in that bed.'

On Friday, which they thought would be payday, they were not paid.

'I'll add it up at the end, all right?' said old Oxted. Karl thought it wasn't such a bad idea; at least they would have a good sum by then. Mike wasn't so sure.

'I bet he buggers off with our money. We've never been told what they're charging us for the room and the food. I reckon they ought to pay *us* for eating that rubbish. If I get another piece of rabbit pie I'll be sick immediately, all over MaOxted's fat belly. Anyhow, dance tomorrow, let's get really pissed.'

They paid to go into the dance. It was in the church hall and there was very little ventilation. The door was surrounded by thick blankets and the windows had blackout curtains over them. Karl felt uncomfortable. He had not brought his decent clothes and only had his school things with him. He had borrowed one of Mike's two ties. He was worried about money, too. If Mike was really going to get drunk it would cost money; they had not been paid and there were still weeks of moneyless life on the farm ahead of them.

Mike, sucking hungrily at his Gold Flake cigarette brought him half a pint.

'Not much talent here I can tell you.' And he was right. There were few girls and huge crowds of soldiers and airmen. Karl rushed up to a girl who was sitting on the side and asked her to dance.

'Sorry, I am sitting this one out,' and then, just after that, she accepted a huge Canadian with a sweet smile. Karl was outraged at such dishonesty. Then there was an 'excuse me' and Karl tapped the soldier on the shoulder. At least he would try to show her what she had missed. The soldier did not even turn his head the first time Karl tapped his shoulder, and the second time he said, 'Fuck off.'

Karl looked at the girl, hoping to see her disgusted by such crudity, but she was gazing at the soldier, enchanted and delighted with his wit. Karl joined Mike, feeling rejected and depressed. Obviously there was no chance of meeting the love of his life here. Mike agreed.

'What have we got to offer? Nothing. They've got their pay and they've got something to talk about. What could we say to a girl? "I'm hoeing on the Oxted farm; I'm going to take my Higher School Certificate next year; one day I'm joining the Forces." No, Karl, we're right out of it, might as well go to our hovel. These tarts are after money and high rank. We've got nothing to offer.'

The next day old Oxted said, 'Harvesting starts today. Kevin, you take the tractor. You two, behind the binder.'

Old Oxted never said anything about Bucko's departure, nothing was ever discussed. He just told the boys what to do.

'That little sod Kevin gets the best jobs, always. I could drive the tractor but I get the binder. You just watch out, Karl, the thistles get up your arm all the time. I remember last year when I helped. Funny how the shitty jobs always go to people like us.'

Mike was really bitterly disappointed. He had had hopes of sitting high up on the tractor. As it was he and Karl followed the binder, which put string round the stooks of corn, and if the string was not on straight or the knot did not hold, they had to re-tie the bundles. After that the stooks had to be stacked in groups of six.

'If you are any good the stooks stay up in a storm,' Bert said. 'Kick them in at the bottom, like so. They stay up for ever. And not too fast, take it easy, there are eight more fields after this.'

Mike and Karl worked together and during the first part of the day they were well ahead of the labourers, but by mid-day they were falling behind. Kevin sneered, 'What's the matter with you two, are you knackered?'

'It's all right for you, sitting on your arse on the tractor,' growled Mike. Come down here and do some real work, you idle sod.'

Kevin just looked ahead and drove on. Karl's arms were covered with scratches from the thistles. In the morning they had thought the labourers were mad, wearing thick coats on a summer's day, now they understood why. There was bread, cheese and tea for lunch, and they could hardly get up to start work again. Karl remembered how his father had liked to retire for a little sleep after lunch. Here it all went on relentlessly.

The binder moved closer and closer to the centre of the field, which would be finished by evening. Occasionally a rabbit darted out, and the labourers would dispatch it with a sharp crack across the neck.

'More rabbit pie,' Mike groaned. Karl saw a rabbit lying on the ground. Its front paws had been cut off by the binder, and it was squealing. Karl just stood and looked. He was so stiff he could not even bend down to finish the creature off. Kevin stopped the tractor, jumped off and killed it with a sharp blow.

'Listen to the bugger squeak,' he said, with some satisfaction, then walked over to another rabbit and prodded it.

Karl shouted, 'Don't torture the poor beast, you cruel sod.'

'Who are you giving orders? Anyroad, it's not my fault, the binder got it. All right, you do it, then.' And Karl tried his hand at rabbit killing. He hit it across the neck and it squealed.

'Who are you calling a cruel sod now?' Kevin asked with some satisfaction, 'You're useless.'

Mike really wanted to drive the tractor. 'Come on, Kevin,' he asked, as persuasively as he could.' Let's have a go on the tractor.'

But Kevin took no notice. Mike was livid. 'I'll kill the little swine next term. You wait, if he so much as nods his head in prayers I'll fetch him such a crack . . .'

Karl reminded Mike that he was building up quite a long list of grievances, but that revenge would be sweet.

'What really gets me is that we can't do anything about him here. Never mind, the harvest is nearly in and it's rick-building next. I've heard a rumour that we'll be on the threshing machine after that.'

They ate lunch with the labourers. Karl particularly liked Ken. He had a square, handsome face, and Karl got a surprise when he took his straw hat off. He was quite bald and suddenly looked much older. Karl said to himself, 'I just hope I never go bald like that. It's awful. I wonder how he feels about it.'

Ken wanted to know what they thought of the Oxteds, and Karl was not sure what to say. After all, Ken and his mate might be great friends of theirs; so he made a non-committal noise. Not so Ken.

'Well, I tell you what I think. They're a miserable bunch of sods. Can't stand them. If it wasn't for the war and not being allowed to change jobs – reserved occupation this, I'm a skilled stablehand, really – I would be off so fast you wouldn't see my arse for dust. Miserable old bleeder. You try getting any cash out of him.'

Karl felt worried. What about his wages?

'You have to have a row with old Oxted just to get the right overtime,' went on Ken. 'He's mean, and the rest of the family's no better. The only one who's all right is in Africa. The money the old man makes; it's marvellous for farmers, is war. They get subsidies galore, they buy up everything and they pay us no wages. I tell you, they'll all be rich when this war is over.'

Karl enjoyed the confidences of Ken and his mates. He liked their contempt of the Oxteds, and also the way they worked. They just kept going, on and on. None of their stooks of corn ever fell down, and when they were making the ricks they finished them off beautifully. They plaited the strands of straw on top, and by the time they had finished, each rick looked like a work of art. Old Oxted just stood by, and they could tell he did not like them finishing off the ricks so beautifully. He wanted them to get on with the next one and not waste his money on what he thought was useless decorations.

Ken talked to Karl in his deep confidential voice. One day he said something about 'When this war is over . . .' Karl had never thought about the war ending. It seemed almost incredible to him that it could, and that the Germans might even be defeated. He thought of all the small nagging impositions they had to put up with. The blackout was perhaps the most irritating of all. Each evening there was the fear that lights might show, and all the extra curtains which had been hung to prevent a glimmer coming through had to be adjusted most carefully.

'Do you know what I'd like to do when the war is over, Ken,' Karl said happily. 'I would like to take a torch and flash it about all over the place, and shine it into the sky at night.'

101

Ken looked troubled. 'Shine torches into the sky? Mustn't do that, it's illegal.'

Karl was really scared. Ken had misunderstood him and thought he wanted to shine a torch into the sky now, while the war was still on.

'Ken, I said that's what I wanted to do when the war is *over*.'

But it was no good. Ken had not really understood. Somehow Karl's foreign accent and his desire to flash lights upwards had reminded him of spies. It seemed to Karl that he was on the verge of reporting him to the police. He knew Karl was not English.

'Where you from, then?' Ken asked. 'Jerry country? What are you doing here? I've got no time for Jerries.'

Karl explained that he had fled from the German government.

'Oh yes, I've read about the refugees – some of them weren't refugees at all, you know. They were spies.'

Karl remembered a cartoon: a paratrooper asked a nun the way and she replied, 'Sorry, I am a parachutist myself.'

'I am not a spy, Ken,' he urged. 'If I was they would have interned me last year.'

But Ken still looked thoughtful and worried. Karl was relieved when Mike came to his rescue.

'Ken, what Karl said was that he'd like to do it *after* the war, as a sort of celebration. Not now. You didn't hear right.'

Ken still looked unconvinced. 'It's illegal,' he grumbled.

Karl was really frightened now. He thought the police would call and take him away for investigation, and that he would land up in an internment camp. All because of that stupid remark. He said to himself that he must learn to be taciturn and not get carried away just because he was enjoying a conversation.

On the last day at the farm, when they were due to go back to school, old Oxted handed each of them a small brown envelope.

'Here you are. I've taken off your board and lodging.'

Karl thought it would be rude to tear the envelope open

102

there and then. He pressed it discreetly, but could not feel the bundle of pound notes he thought ought to be there. He and Mike were embarrassed, and old Oxted did not help. His fishy eyes seemed gloomier than ever.

'Rained a lot this summer,' was his only comment after six weeks of what the boys thought had been hard work. And not only the work. They *had* helped to get the harvest in. A word of appreciation, perhaps? But old Oxted just shuffled off and they tore the envelopes open. Karl's had seventeen shillings and nine pence in it and Mike's just over eighteen. They were not just angry they were beside themselves. They jumped up and down and stamped their boots on the floor – anything to make their rage worse, and let off steam.

'The shit! The exploiting bastard,' Mike shouted. 'Six weeks of work, bad food and that bed and he gives us this. I'd like to burn his farm down.'

Karl felt equally angry and disappointed, but Mike's rage frightened him. He still remembered the conversation with Ken and he was afraid they would be arrested for threatening arson. Mike went on, 'The only one who had any sense was old Bucko. He left in good time. I bet he spent the whole summer touching up barmaids' tits. What have we got to show for all our work? The chiselling sod.'

They were walking past a tractor, the one that Kevin had been driving during the harvest. They both pissed all over the blanket on the tractor seat, and felt better.

'That should keep his arse nice and warm next time he rides his precious tractor,' gloated Mike.

They went into the orchard, took a couple of sticks and knocked apples off one of the trees until Mike said, 'Stop! I bet he gets a government subsidy on his apples, and if the crop fails they'll pay him compensation. Come on, don't let's bother with him any more, just concentrate our efforts on getting Kevin when he comes back to school.'

Their rage and disappointment evaporated and two days later, when Karl saw Kevin in prayers, none of it seemed to matter. Kevin looked a bit apprehensive, but all Karl said was, 'Your ma all right, Kevin?'

Steve wanted to know how he had got on in the summer, and Karl launched on a passionate account of all the injustices they had had to suffer, and what a burden it was being an exploited juvenile labourer. Steve seemed amused.

'Do you know, I had to leave school when I was twelve and I worked on a bread van. When the headmaster heard about it he took me back and charged no fees. You see I had no family. My parents dumped me on an uncle who had to look after me although he didn't want to. Wages were even worse then, specially for farm workers. Have you heard of tied cottages? I know of labourers who were turned out of their cottages because they voted for Lloyd George. Whole families had to get out, just for voting Liberal.'

Karl was astounded. This Steve, so polished, so much in command in his own white drawing room, with its modern paintings on the wall; this Steve, standing by the elegant Georgian fireplace, had once been on a bread van? Rejected by his family? Karl was completely amazed. Even Ben, who knew everything, had not told him that. Karl understood now why Steve and his wife had taken in so many refugees. They understood what it meant to be without a home and a family.

Now Karl began to see more clearly why Steve talked about the role of the family in the way he did. He was always at pains to make the point that the family was not the only unit in which a child could be successfully brought up. Karl now understood that Steve's apparent detachment, which up till now he had found unpleasantly cold-blooded, could be seen as a way of saying that there were alternatives to the stifling atmosphere of the family. Perhaps it was better to work on a farm and do rotten jobs, than be the darling of over-possessive parents. Karl, in spite of his loneliness now, could well remember how stifled he had been sometimes when he was with the Levi grandmother. She had so smothered him that he felt he could hardly breathe; and he was an outsider, a distant relative, not her own child. Perhaps anything was better than that. He got the impression that Steve was telling him: 'Stop feeling sorry for yourself. Things could be a lot worse, and they are much better now than they used to be.' Steve didn't believe in saying things too directly. He preferred making oblique remarks, which Karl could interpret as he wished. Karl found this way much easier to bear. Direct instruction, being told what to do and how to think was difficult for him. Something rose inside him and blocked the words out of his mind. He would not listen, but daydreamed, or listened only for a weakness in the argument that would give him a chance to pull it to pieces. Paul had said to him once: 'You're very destructive, Karl – when you're on the attack, your jokes are good, but nothing is safe from them. You are a nihilist.'

Steve's comments seemed to be helping Karl to think more positively. 'At least I didn't cost anyone any money during the holiday,' he thought. 'I've been independent and I stuck it out – but I'm still glad we pissed on that blanket. I hope the Oxteds got wet arses.'

Steve talked to him about his history syllabus and the forth-coming exams.

'At the end of the term we'll put you in for a Cambridge scholarship. Ben is to try for King's; Paul, will sit for my own college. Do you know, Karl, I didn't have any money at all for my education. By the time I left Cambridge I was three hundred pounds in debt, and the first thing I had to do was pay back that money. I got a job in an extraordinary school, but with the money I saved I managed to pay off that debt.'

Again Karl realized that this was Steve's way of talking to him about his own money problems. Here was the answer to his anxious question about how much Cambridge would cost. 'Never mind about money. Go ahead. The money will turn up and if you have to borrow you can always pay it back later.' Karl wondered if he worried about being in debt because of all the things his father had said to him. The old banker was very firm about debt; certainly not as casual about it as Steve. On more than one occasion he had said to Karl, 'Once you are in debt you lose the power of self-determination, others have con-trol over your fate. One thing I have always avoided was being in debt. Not that it's always good policy, mind. When inflation was at its worst in the 1920s the value of money tumbled and it was better to owe. You could easily have paid back any debt with worthless money; but I don't think it would have been an honourable thing to do.'

And that, Karl thought now, is the attitude to life that made you stay behind and suffer, if you are still alive. Steve's argument made sense, but it was a solution his family would have called 'bohemian' or 'not solidly respectable'. 'What the hell,' he thought. 'Who is respectable, anyhow. Is six weeks of farm work respectable?'

Now, suddenly he was faced with the possibility of getting a scholarship to Cambridge. Karl did not feel as confident as Ben, who was already calculating how much he would get if he won a major scholarship and whether he should read history or something else (Karl had learnt that one 'read' a subject). As always he was amazed by Ben's point of view.

'It's terribly important for the Steves that we get into Cambridge,' he explained, 'and preferably one of the "better" colleges. To them, it's a political issue; they want the halls of privilege to be stormed by people like us, nobodies who have nothing to offer but our ability. If we establish the precedent more can come after us. Probably Hugh is more important than any of us. After all, his father only has a grocer's shop, and most of us came from what they call the "professional classes". Of course, none of us is as stinking rich as the Hartlands, but then no one is perfect.'

Before going to Cambridge Karl had to report to the police to let them know that he would be away for a few days. As always he produced his grey alien's registration book. The sergeant knew Karl, and said cheerfully, 'Cambridge this time, eh? They are sending you up for an exam? Well done, they must think you are clever. Well I hope you do well. Good luck.'

In Cambridge Karl eventually found Corpus Christi College, with its imposing, Victorian entrance. Isobel had told Karl that Victorian architecture was a disaster. 'They had no respect for the past,' she said, 'and were terribly arrogant, which meant they just knocked everything down, or worse, restored it. A whole medieval heritage was destroyed by engineers and

106

speculators. There is one college they built which is so awful that a society has been founded for its destruction; the membership fee is one brick taken from the walls, and the members reckon that if enough people join the college will collapse.'

By the time Karl went up for his exam, Isobel was already in her first year at Girton. 'Another Victorian barn,' she had written, 'you should see the dim corridors.' She had also wished him luck, and said she hoped that he would come 'up'. Karl gathered that Cambridge was superior to anywhere else because to get to it you always came 'up', and then went 'down' from it.

The porter looked down the list. 'Hartland – B 7 – turn left, second staircase, the door's open.'

He did not even look up. Karl only had a very small case, just things for a couple of days, and he found the room easily. The two doors were intriguing. Little Ted had explained about them, and the practice known as 'sporting your oak'. If you did not wish to be disturbed you shut both doors, and then visitors knew they were not welcome.

'Mind you,' Little Ted added, 'once in a while, if people didn't like someone, they would burn the doors down.'

Ben, who was already familiar with the history and institutions of the University added, 'In your college, Corpus, they built the bathrooms out of money obtained from fines imposed when the students wrecked the Master's rooms.'

Karl explored, and found the bathrooms. There were huge bathtubs surrounded by pine planks and fitted with vast brass taps. It seemed strange to Karl that, in an institution that was rated to be the bastion of privilege and wealth, one had to cross two open courtyards in order to keep clean or go to the lavatory. His room obviously belonged to someone else, and had just been vacated to make room for examination candidates. Everything was brown, cream and dark green, and filthy football socks stuck out of a drawer. The books seemed to indicate that the real occupant was an engineer. Karl spread his notes and old essays out and re-read them feverishly.

'Remember,' Steve had said, 'it is not a test of knowledge so

107

much as a test of what you make of the information you have gathered. They are looking for information about your general interests and testing your analytical ability, they don't just want a regurgitation of crammed facts.'

Karl looked at his Luther essay. He, too, felt like whistling to keep up his courage. The dark Gothic palace depressed him no end. He looked into the court, and there stood two huge water tanks supported by sandbags. The windows were either sandbagged or taped. A figure in a short black gown went across the square. Not on the grass. 'Only dons are allowed on the grass,' Karl had been told. Supper was eaten in a Gothic dining hall, where portraits of eighteenth-century clergymen looked down, and the plates had the college crest on them. His neighbour was not very talkative.

'You here for the examinations?' Karl asked.

'Yes.'

'Have you come from far?'

'Winchester. And you?'

'Elmfield.'

'Oh.'

Karl had learnt to interpret the various meanings of the word 'oh'. This time it meant 'never heard of it in my life', and was certainly not designed to inspire further conversation. Karl recalled Isobel saying 'At university, it's the talk, the interchange of ideas that matters. You meet new and exciting people with experience of life quite different from your own.' Well, it didn't look as if it was going to be like that this evening.

A note dropped through Karl's letterbox. A crested little square note; the same crest as the one on his soup plate. 'Would Mr' – ('yes, "Mr",' Karl thought. 'What a grand place where a mere schoolboy was "Mr" and "sir" to the porters') – 'Would Mr Hartland call on Dr Hardstone tomorrow morning at eleven.' Karl knew of the Doctor. He had read his interpretation of Jacobean politics in preparation for the meeting. He also knew he was an MP. Steve had briefed him most carefully.

'You may meet Hardstone, a difficult man with very unfortunate views. One of the hardcore of Cambridge Tories. Try to keep off politics. Let him know about your extensive knowledge of painting, and if you get a chance, make sure he knows you have read his books.'

Karl knocked on the door. The Doctor was standing by the fireplace. He was wearing a wing collar, black bow-tie, striped trousers and gold-rimmed glasses. He looked grey and malevolent.

'Hartland, Elmfield? Sit down. So you are from Germany?'

Karl said 'sir' very easily – this was the sort of man you called 'sir' without hesitation. He was terrified, he had never met anyone who wrote books before, let alone a Member of Parliament.

'He has never held office,' Steve had told him. 'Too difficult; and he has an unfortunate tendency to correct the Members' English.'

Karl explained that 'Come from Germany' would not do.

'I came as a refugee.'

'Of course.' The Doctor was irritated, and his tone seemed to say, 'every fool knows that'. Karl noticed the pages of a manuscript he was writing lying on the table.

'Why did you come to this country, Hartland?'

Karl wanted to say, 'Because they put a label round my neck and put me on a train,' but he did not think that would be the right answer.

'I have a great admiration for the institutions of this country.'

Evidently not the right answer, either. The Doctor gave a series of spluttering coughs. Karl could see he was in pain, heaving up and down with the coughing. Later he learnt that the Doctor had been gassed in the First War, but at the time he was inclined to think it was his answer that had caused the agonized paroxysms. Karl thought that perhaps the sort of self-governing democracy practised at Elmfield was not the sort of government Doctor Hardstone admired. The fit of coughing subsided and the Doctor went on.

'Hartland, who is in the majority?'

Karl felt a bold statement was indicated. 'The workers, sir?'

'No, the dead. There are more dead souls in this country than live ones.'

His expression seemed to say, 'Didn't you know that, you idiot?' Abruptly he changed the subject, rephrasing his question about why Karl had come to England.

'What I meant was that, as a Jew, surely you would have chosen to go to Palestine. Why didn't you?'

'My family were not Zionists. I don't think they believed in the ideas of the movement. They identified themselves more with the fate of Germany until the National Socialists rejected them.'

'So, what you are saying is that the Jews have no business in Palestine.'

'No, I am not. I am saying that my family did not want to go there.'

This was a minefield, and Karl knew it. Steve had warned him that the Doctor was on a pro-Arab House of Commons Committee. But he felt passionately that Jews should be allowed to go anywhere they chose to escape from Nazi persecution.

The Doctor turned to a deeper issue still.

'The Arabs. What about them? Have they no rights?'

Karl sensed that what was wanted was a more spirited argument. No 'correct' answer was expected of him, but the Doctor did not want him to wilt under the challenging questioning. They went on to reading.

'What have you read lately?'

Karl had been entranced by Gibbon, particularly his amusing attack on the follies of institutionalized Christianity. Vanessa's Rationalism had begun to have a deep influence on him. But this was obviously not the book to have mentioned. Doctor Hardstone snorted, 'Atheistic circus horse. Poppycock!'

Would Toynbee fare any better?

'I can't stand these unresearched, over-generalized prophetic outpourings.'

Daunted, Karl thought that this might be the moment to indicate that he had read Hardstone's own book, but then decided that was too obvious and pathetic. It was better to defend what he knew was not popular. As Karl was dismissed from the room, the Doctor asked a final question.

'Have you been to the Fitzwilliam Museum yet? I recommend

110

it. Look at the carpets on the floor, I saw to it that they were put there. Carpets are meant to be walked on.'

Karl fervently wanted to promise that he would walk on the carpets, but he was just dismissed with a wave. He looked, and wondered if he could see something like a smile on the pained, white face. He said 'goodbye', but this triviality was completely ignored.

Some days later Steve called Karl in. He was smiling. 'They didn't give you an award, but they said a number of your papers were up to scholarship standard and they will be prepared to take you when you come out of the army. Karl, you have done terribly well. Some months ago I would not have even considered you as scholarship material. I suggest you try again. We may get a better award at another college.'

Karl felt a desperate sense of failure and disappointment. He could not understand why Steve smiled at him. The waste. Several pounds for fees and fares, and now nothing but a nice letter. What made it worse was that Ben had won a major scholarship. Vanessa also praised him.

'You have done so well, Karl; you even seemed to have made an impression on the redoubtable Hardstone. What more do you want?'

She sensed Karl's disappointment. Karl just said, 'thank you' miserably, and decided there and then that this was the last examination he would take. He would leave school, go and stay with the Levis and try to get into the army.

Chapter 6

All around Karl there was jubilation and rejoicing. 'Four scholarships,' they kept on saying, 'four scholarships. It's in *The Times*! Elmfield's on the map, now.'

'It's all right for them,' Karl thought, 'they may be on the map but I am not.' The disappointment was difficult to hide. He had to smile, to congratulate and make appreciative noises; it was almost unbearable, particularly with Ben. He had won two scholarships, one at Cambridge and one at Oxford and now had to make the delicious decision as to which one he would take.

'I think I'll go to Oxford, I prefer the style of the philosophy teaching there, and the architecture is more appealing.'

'God,' thought Karl, 'the conceited sod, the unbearably arrogant swine! He can choose to go where he wants and will never have to accept a place gratefully if it's offered to him as I will. The despicable turd has got two scholarships, and his name will go up in golden Gothic letters on the board in the Hall, while my name will be nowhere.'

All he actually managed to say was, 'I can't think what you see in Oxford after the beauty of King's.' And they continued to argue about the respective attractions of the architecture. The argument was fierce because Karl was so disappointed, and possibly Ben sensed this. Karl went on, 'It's all a waste of time; we'll all be dead, anyhow. Do you know what, the next thing I am going to do is get into the Forces and do something worthwhile. Here we are, piddling around with scholarships while there's a war on which we just ignore. We'll all be dead, don't you see?'

'Oh no we won't; *I* won't, anyhow. I can't see the point of rushing into danger – this death wish. I intend to have a nice career at a famous University. All I need now is a first. A first and a fellowship at All Souls – good claret for the rest of my life.'

Karl was furious, as always, at Ben's assurance. He resented his ability to plan ahead and, what was worse, the knowledge that Ben would never have any difficulty in living up to his boasts.

But Karl couldn't go on envying Ben for ever, he had his own decisions to make. Steve wanted to talk to him. 'Look here, Karl,' – he always said that when he had something important to say, and it irritated Karl, who said to himself, 'I *am* looking, you silly sod' – 'Look here, Karl, you have done splendidly; we had never thought . . .'

'Here he goes again, praising me for nothing,' Karl thought. He still could not accept the honest and genuine good will of the man. He even reacted angrily to statements that were intended to make him value his own worth.

'Steve can't see that I am a failure. It was a scholarship or nothing for me. There is no money, doesn't he understand that? The very shoes I am wearing, this grey suit, were given to me by a charity. My sister had to go and ask nicely, and of course they were generous, but I have to accept charity now when not so long ago our family contributed to charities.'

Steve went on, 'I want you to try for Oxford next. I'll put my shirt on your getting something this time. I had a talk with the tutor of the college that has just taken Hugh and they are interested. "Send us your good boys, Mr Stevens," he said, "we don't care what school they come from, we want the best, and your boys seem remarkably well taught and perceptive." Now I want you to try, Karl; they will understand that it has not been easy for you.'

'Can't you see,' Karl wanted to say, 'I don't want allowances made; I want to be accepted either because I am me, or because I am so good that they recognize it. It's like these shoes, I hate them because they were given to me. They were given kindly and tactfully, but I hate them. If I try for Oxford it will cost more money, more time at school. Let me go!'

Karl said he would like to try, but would prefer to do it out of school. He thought perhaps he might stay in London. He did not want to reject Steve's faith in him, but he wanted to be on his own.

Ben was cutting when Karl told him his plan.

'Work in London? You must be mad. You'll spend all your time daydreaming, and mooning over whoever you happen to think you're in love with when you get there. You need the quiet of this place. Steve and Vanessa's support and the criticism of your essays they can give you. Go on, stay here until you have to go into the Forces. No one will make you go, you know. They don't call non-British subjects up. If they don't want me, I'm certainly not going to stick my neck out. Where would you stay if you went to London? With that rich relative with all those paintings in the house – and the daughter?'

Karl knew that Ben was right but he could not convey to him his hatred of being under an obligation to anyone, his disgust at his own failure – he could only feel jealous of the few who had succeeded so outstandingly. He entirely ignored the majority, the sixty or so boys who had quietly left the school to go into banks, offices or wherever. *Careers for Public School Boys*, was the title of a book on the table in the library at Elmfield. It had been left there by accident, and Karl had looked at it – even though Elmfield was not a public school at all. Elmfield boys were entitled to have careers, he grumbled. But the contents were not too cheering. There was timber to be felled and transported in Malaysia – only the Japanese had taken over there. Civil Service in the Empire – Karl could almost hear the answers, 'Sorry, but only British subjects . . .', 'Oh, you were not born here, in that case why don't you . . .'

He remembered a talk given by a high-ranking army officer who had come to the school to recruit for the Tank Corps.

'We need keen chaps like you from the Grammar Schools to man the tanks. I was with Monty at Alamein, and I can tell you, the tanks were there. They are the weapon of the future.'

He had rows of ribbons which Karl studied enviously, and best of all he had only one eye, the other being covered with a black patch. Karl spotted the Distinguished Service Order on the man's chest. He went up to him after the lecture, which had been about the function of the tank in desert warfare.

'Please, sir, I would like to join the Tank Corps.'

'Oh, yes, jolly good. Well, get in touch with the Recruiting Office . . .'

'Please sir, there is one difficulty. I was not born in this country.'

'Oh that's all right, lots of chaps weren't born in this country, parents abroad and that sort of thing.'

'No, you see I was born in Germany and I only came over in 1939.'

'Germany? Oh, well that's different. What are you doing here, then?' He looked at Karl suspiciously, a bit puzzled; perhaps even annoyed at such impudence.

'You see, sir, the Germans threw us out. I mean I was sent out and I want to fight the Nazis.'

'Yes, well . . . but this is unusual. You'll have to ask the War Office . . .' He turned away from Karl to the next eager applicant and Karl could tell that the interview was at an end. His chances of wearing the glamorous black beret were nil.

But Karl had made up his mind. He had to leave school. He asked his sister if it was all right. Could he stay with the Levis? They had invited him, but did they mean it? He would work for the next scholarship examination, but he intended to go into the army as soon as possible. He told Steve of his decision, and if Steve was disappointed he did not show it. It was not long before Karl was saying goodbye to members of staff.

'Oh, goodbye, Hartland. Leaving us? Well, you've done jolly well here. Into the Forces next?'

'Yes, sir. Actually, I would like to get into the Tank Corps.'

Karl liked saying 'actually'. He had heard officers say it and had practised the intonation. It sounded right by now. So did most of his pronunciation. Over the months the transformation he had worked so hard for had happened. Fewer and fewer people asked, 'And where are you from?' And even better, they did not even compliment him on his good English.

'Well, all the best, Hartland, and good luck with your army career. I expect you will be in officer's uniform when we see you here next. Do look us up.'

And, at dinner-time, Steve banged his teacup with a spoon.

'I have got a sad duty today. We must all say goodbye to Karl. He has not been with us all that long, but we have appreciated his sense of humour and he has done a great deal of very good work in the House. I am amazed at the progress he has made here . . .'

Karl could feel himself blushing deeply. He looked down into his plate and stared at his piece of bread and marge. It was nice to be appreciated, and he suddenly felt miserable about leaving Elmfield. It was a good place and had helped him enormously. To think that he had come not knowing more than a few words of English, and now he was leaving with a Higher Certificate in four subjects and the promise of a place at university. But the rancour was still there. Why no scholarship for him? All right, that wasn't Steve's fault, but he had raised Karl's hopes too high. Suddenly, Karl remembered the geography master saying, 'Perhaps we will see you in officer's uniform.' That was a thought. A polished Sam Browne belt, one sparkling pip on each shoulder. He could carry his cane under his arm . . .'

Then his attention returned to Steve, who was saying, 'We have been lucky to have Karl with us. He has helped to make the sixth form a forum for intelligent discussion, and in the House we have learnt to appreciate . . .'

Karl did not dare to look across at Axford, who had not become any lovelier or easier to get on with. They had avoided each other and at least not had any more great rows. Steve finished what seemed to Karl to be something like a funeral oration, and one of the younger boys called 'Three cheers for Karl!'

They cheered, and Karl felt close to tears. They had cheered him, and they had sounded as if they meant it, and after all the awful things he had done. Karl remembered how much he had feared being hissed by the younger boys. That had been his principal nightmare, being followed by dozens of small boys all hissing and booing.

'Speech,' they shouted, 'Speech.' And Karl got up with some confidence. After all, had he not learned to make passionate speeches about fox-hunting and the rights of women at the debating society?

'I would like to thank you all for your cheers, for your friendship . . .'

Karl had half-expected to be asked to make a leaver's speech. He wanted to be urbane and witty. He wanted to thank everyone for putting up with a snotty, aggressive refugee boy who had come from nowhere and whom they had taught to be reasonably fair, and who had learnt to exercise authority without the continuous threat of punishment. Karl was never quite sure how it had happened, but by now the younger boys, and even the fifth formers, had given up arguing with him all the time – and it was not just because he would threaten to fight them. He wanted to talk about authority and relationships the way Steve did, but now it would not come out. He might have said, 'I am scared of leaving here but I must. I can't cost everyone loads of money and do nothing in return. I have not even won a scholarship. I will go into the army, though. I don't really know why, but it seems to be what is expected of young men. A lady in a bus said to me the other day. "Why aren't you in the army?" and I was ashamed. All I had done was fail to offer her my seat because I had not noticed her. So I will go into the army; and when I have distinguished myself I will come back. Then you can admire my smart uniform while I tell you how I won the war.' Actually, all he managed to do was to choke out the words, 'I have been very happy here and I will be very sorry to leave school.' And they cheered again.

Karl was handed his last report. His understanding of European history seemed to have deepened, and he had contributed to the life of the House and the school. Everyone wished him well. He gave the report to his sister when he went to London.

'Well, little baby bunny rabbit brother that *is* a nice report.'

'Nice,' Karl thought, 'it's bloody marvellous when you consider my awful reports in Germany. There all the teachers had written, "satisfactory", for every subject, except for physical training. In that, Karl was thought to be "inadequate". His parents had always been kind about his reports. What had worried them most was that his form master wrote "precocious" at the bottom of the report every year. Karl wondered whether he had now stopped being precocious.

'Anyhow,' his sister continued, 'when you go to the Levis' show Walter the report. He may be pleased, and will want to tell his sister that she has got her money's worth. Has it ever occurred to you to thank the relations for all the money they have given you?'

Karl was furious. It had not occurred to him to say 'thank you' formally; and his sister's rebuke aroused all his resentments. 'Why should I thank them?' he thought. 'They are rolling in money. They got it all out by some fiddle and now I am supposed to lick their boots in gratitude. I had so little money to spend I could not even have a half-bottle of milk in the evening; and I worked on that shitty farm to save them money.'

All his old dislike of his sister rose up in him. 'Why,' he thought, 'does she tell me to write thank you letters as if I was a ten year old who's been asked to a birthday party. I am sick to death of all her "baby brother" stuff and the way she tries to boss me around.'

But Karl was also a bit afraid of her. He knew that he depended on her; and she really was doing her best for him. If only she would not push him, so that he ended up hating her for what she was trying so decently to do for him. So he just stood there looking sulky, and she went on.

'If only your poor father could see the report. He did not think you would ever do well at school. Have you any idea how much he used to worry about your school work?'

'Oh god,' thought Karl, 'now she's bringing in the family bit. She's going to remind me that we have the same parents, are of good family and that I must be a good boy. If I am not careful she will ask me to hold my foot up so that everyone can see the nice shoes I got from the charity organization – it's going to be one long round of embarrassment. All I need is for her to call me her baby bunny rabbit brother in front of the Levis and everything will be marvellous. I can just see Hannah's face when she hears it. If only I could get into the army now, but it's bound to be months.'

Margot went on undeterred. 'Have you seen Vati's letter? It came via the Swiss Red Cross and it's very old. Have you written?'

Karl had not, he had just given up. He could not communicate through a form on which phrases had to be underlined. What he was even more guilty about was the sense of relief he felt that his father was no longer able to nag him. 'Have you done any geometry from that book I sent you?' He had worked as hard as he could but the admonishing voice still sounded in his ears and he felt uneasy when he just played about or sat and daydreamed. Now Karl thought his sister was trying to come in on the act; she, too, was trying to make him feel guilty. First her implied reproach about the thank you letter, and now the mention of the letter from their father. She showed him the Red Cross letter. About the only thing that was familiar was the signature. They were all well, it said, and looked forward to hearing from them. But the letter was so old.

'I wonder what is happening to them,' Margot said sadly. 'We hear such terrible stories, I just hope they aren't true. Everything in Germany must be in chaos now, and I can't imagine how the old people will survive. I wish we could send them something . . .'

Karl wanted to comfort his sister so he repeated what he had heard at Elmfield.

'A lot of it is propaganda, you know. In the First War they accused the Germans of all sorts of atrocities that turned out to be untrue.'

Margot looked at Karl. 'Funny, bunny rabbit, at times you sound exactly like father and you look like him. Of course, you did not know him as well as I did, you were so young when you left.'

Suddenly it was all right and Karl liked his sister again. The family bond was strong and he had to admit to himself that she was having a difficult time. Her work in the factory was tiring and not very pleasant. Even ordinary living was not easy.

Margot went on, 'One of the worst things is the shopping. All the best things are gone by the time I get to the shops. The other day the grocer had tinned pineapple, which you can get on points, but by the time I got there he said, "Sorry, ducks, you are too late." It's all right for Alice, she works in an office and old Loewenberg, her boss, lets her go any time. She does some shopping for me. She really is decent. She asked about you the other day; "How is that beautiful brother of yours?" She wanted to know if I thought she should take you in hand and "educate" you.'

Karl giggled, slightly embarrassed, but at the same time he realized he was enjoying being with his sister. He looked forward to going to the Levis. Luxury and a bowl of egg sandwich spread were waiting for him.

Margot went on, 'Walter Levi has really been very nice to us. He says you are welcome to stay with them as long as you need to. He says you can sleep in Fred's room while he is away at school and, if you want, you can work for another scholarship.'

'I don't think so,' said Karl, 'I am seriously thinking of going into the army now.'

Margot appeared not to have heard. 'Do you know,' she said, 'sometimes I can see our mother in your face. You aren't only like Father, your chin and your freckles are Mother's. She hated having freckles, you know. Used to put cucumber on her face and milk lotions.'

Karl was irritated again. He had made a momentous announcement, that he would go into the army, and all Margot did was to go on about his sodding chin and his mother. He looked at his sister.

'Odd,' he thought, 'that we both come from the same mother, that we have the same background and that we know the same things about people. Families are strange, and I am not used to being in one any more. What irritates me is this continual

120

tugging at my emotional strings. It seems impossible to talk about anything without arousing great feelings of either anger or love in both of us. An odd relationship.'

What Karl hated was being dependent on others. Having to be nice, *and* being reminded that as long as he was nice there would always be a bed in a mock Tudor house for him. He was quite unable to see his sister simply as his sister, and he couldn't say the words he wanted to . . . 'I would like to get on with you. You are all I have in this world.'

Deep down, Karl knew that he would never see his father again or any of their other relatives. He dared not say so, though, because it would upset his sister, and because *he* could not bear to dwell on it, either.

'Come on, baby brother,' Margot chivvied, 'don't look so hurt. I didn't mean to upset you. Come on, I'll take you to the Levis. You will be very happy there. You can call him "Walter", by the way, he is a relation.'

Karl noticed that by the time they got to the Levi house his sister had perked up. She no longer looked strained and irritable. Walter Levi received them at the door.

'Yes,' his sister said graciously, 'I would love a cup of coffee. Well here he is, here's my baby brother, I hope he behaves himself while he is here.'

'There she goes again. If she goes on like that I'll piss on the Rembrandt etching,' fumed Karl.

Margot produced the report from Elmfield for Walter's inspection. He put his glasses on and read it carefully. Karl looked at him while he was reading. Yes, he did look rather distinguished; he liked the way he put his thick horn-rimmed glasses on with an elegant swoop.

Margot had told him before they set out, 'I asked Alice to look at his handwriting. You know, she understands handwriting amazingly, she has an intuitive understanding, just one look, and then she moves the paper about. When I showed her Walter's handwriting she said, and you must understand she had no idea whose writing it was, "a very able and distinguished man, he has money, and an instinct for dealing with money matters, but he would not be a good man to have as an enemy;

there is a streak of ruthlessness there. But humour, too, and a sense of irony." '

Karl was sceptical. Surely, as Alice knew Margot knew Walter Levi, she would guess that it was his handwriting. This attitude didn't please his sister, though. 'Don't always try to be so clever,' she snapped irritably.

Walter had finished the report. 'It's good, isn't it? You can tell it is a good school from the way they take a genuine interest in you. I wish my children got such reports. You should see Hannah's. What that madam gets away with! Really, the schools here are much more tolerant than they were in Germany. When I think of my poor brother who was killed in the First War; well, they expelled him and so my parents sent him as a boarder to a Lutheran Pastor, and do you know . . .' Walter raised his eyebrows, seeming to apologize to Margot for the indelicacy of the statement he was about to make '. . . he had not been there more than a few days when he got the Pastor's daughter pregnant – as the English would say, "got her in the family way". It cost my father a packet to arrange for a little operation – they told everyone it was for beauty treatment.'

He smiled at Karl. 'We are all looking forward to having you with us. Do you know what Hannah said after you left last time? "They may come again." That is high praise from my daughter, who is very unkind about the majority of my friends. You will have Fred's room. I hope you won't mind sleeping on the couch while he is home for the holidays. It won't be for more than a few more days now. I don't know, but the more you pay for the schooling of your children in this country the longer the holidays they get. Your social life, Karl, begins tomorrow; all three of you have been invited next door to a party. One thing about this neighbourhood, we have very distinguished people living around us. Next door, the man is something in the City, an old Harrovian, a complete and absolute drunkard. There was a tremendous row outside the other night. I looked out of the window and was startled to see our distinguished neighbour in his wife's carrot bed, pulling them up, shouting and bawling. She was there, poor thing, trying to stop him.'

122

Karl, well versed in the symbolism of Freud, laughed uproariously and Walter looked at him, amused, 'Yes, I too wondered how a psychiatrist would have interpreted his actions.'

Karl observed, 'Possibly an unconscious expression of jealousy.'

Walter was pleased. 'At last! Someone in this family with a sense of humour. Actually, I can't say that Hannah hasn't got one. She is not averse to a risqué remark, and knows a lot more than she is supposed to at her age, which is a bit dangerous. No, it's Fred I'm worried about. He gets all embarrassed and says, "Please, Dad, don't make jokes like that." Well Karl,' he went on, changing the subject, 'now that you are here, what are your plans?'

Karl explained that he was going to try for another scholarship, but inside himself he was saying, 'Oh no, I am not, I am sick to death of school work. I want to get away from it all, go into the army and do a man's job – God, I sound like a bloody recruiting poster!'

Walter was interested. 'Well, here are my books.' He pointed to several well filled bookshelves. 'Use any you want. I am not a great one for reading; it is odd, no one in my family reads much. There is one exception, my cousin, who is now a well known professor in the States. My father paid for his education, but they had the most frightful row. Peter said the war (that's the 1914 one) was a nonsense and Germany was bound to lose and he would have no part of it. My father rose to his full height, not very high, he was only just over five foot, but a man not used to being contradicted (you saw his portrait at my mother's flat didn't you?) He showed Peter the door and Peter has never been in touch with the family since. A typical intellectual, no sense of obligation or gratitude.'

'That makes two of us,' Karl thought, and wished fervently that he might be as brilliant as the cousin.

Walter continued, 'I'll tell you about him. When he was a boy he had a grandmother who was blind, so when she was in the room by herself he would switch the light off. "You don't need that, Omi," he would say. A ruthless child.'

Karl could not quite see the moral of the tale; it seemed a

logical thing to do. He suddenly realized that whatever Walter said, he took the opposite view. But he was also charmed by the man. His urbane manner. Each tale he told seemed to be vastly witty and he addressed Karl as if he was a person of some importance and maturity.

'The books . . .' Walter went back to the beginning of the conversation, '. . . yes, just help yourself. I have got a beautiful Goethe, first edition, here. You must look at that later on. No one in this house seems very interested. Do you know, I am impressed with the way you have settled down to your work at school.'

Karl thought, 'that was easy, I had no alternative.'

'That is the thing about the younger generation, they have a sense of purpose. Now my brother, whom I just mentioned . . .'

Karl was really interested in the brother. He sounded an unusual man. 'He was a rogue. He was the bad one in the family and I was the good boy. When I was a young man he was my idol. I adored him but he never took much notice of me. Except when he was tired of a girl. Then he would slip me a few gold coins and say, "Take her off my back, for god's sake; take her out, anything. I can't stand her any more." My father was in despair. Everything my brother did infuriated him. Perhaps his good looks were to blame. No one, certainly no woman, could ever say "no" to him, and my mother and Eunice, that is your aunt Eunice, spoilt him and tried to protect him from father's rage. The war was a kind of release for him. It came just in time. The trouble at home was getting worse – dud cheques and that sort of thing.' – Karl wondered if Walter's brother had forged signatures, as he had done when he was twelve – 'Well, the day war broke out he volunteered for the Bavarian Guards and they took him although he was a Jew. In those days Jews could not join the 'better' regiments. I believe it is the same here – no Jews are allowed in the Guards; but the Bavarian Guards had a tremendous reputation. "My Bavarian Lions" the Kaiser had called them. Within a few weeks my brother had won the Iron Cross, not Second Class either, the Iron Cross First Class, the first Iron Cross won in Berlin, and by a Jew.'

124

Walter gave one of his little laughs, 'Amazing. Do you know we were proud, really proud. Considering what has happened since it really is funny. Anyhow, my brother was not particularly proud of the family, I can tell you that. To me he said, "You little swine, I suppose you will crawl up Father's arse until you inherit the family fortune," and he said to Father, "You corrupt little man, you and your dirty deals." I suppose he might have been a communist, but he was not really a political sort of person. And poor Eunice, she made him a little bag and put bandages and iodine into it, in case he got hurt. He just laughed and said, "The wounds you get out there, you could stick the whole bag into them." She meant well and it was unkind of him, but then no one at home understood what was going on at the Front. Once he told me that he was in a bayonet charge and he stuck his bayonet into a Frenchman who said "Schma Ysroel" just before he died – that really upset him. He was used to killing people, but to know that he had killed another Jew, that upset him.'

Karl wondered if he would have felt any better had the man shouted, 'Jesus Christ', but he kept the thought to himself.

Walter was in full flow now. 'Well, he died. He did something terribly brave, I think he was after the Pour Le Mérite, that's the German Victoria Cross. He wanted to prove that he was some use. I was talking to Eunice and she said, "Walter, it's just as well he is dead; he would never have fitted into the world of our father and the family. I think he wanted to die." She was right, there would have been all sorts of trouble and I think he would have ended up in prison. But he was a beautiful man, I admired him very much.'

Karl hoped Walter would go on with his stories about the family. They were certainly an odd lot, he thought, remembering the visit to Walter's mother.

After lunch Walter asked Karl to walk round the garden with him. 'Do you like the garden? We have a real character to look after it. He comes when he feels like it. He eats all the onions, you can't get within yards of him without smelling them on his breath, and poor Frauelein von Seydlitz is absolutely terrified of him. I think she fears a fate worse than death when old Watkins is around. He doesn't seem to have a home, and we think he sleeps in air raid shelters.'

Walter's voice dropped slightly. It always did when a matter of some confidentiality or delicacy was to be discussed. 'Fred is looking forward to seeing you. He needs company, someone to bring him out. I don't know why, but he is depressed. It's the family, I'm afraid. You should meet his mother's family.'

Karl thought, 'Well, yours is not all that average, either.'

'His mother – I told you we were divorced? Well, her family – what a bunch of *meschuggeneh*. Do you still know what that means? Of course one must distinguish between *meschuggeh* and downright madness, I know that.'

Walter talked on. He was excited and Karl could not and did not want to interrupt. He was flattered that an adult was speaking to him about such intimate matters, that he was being treated as an equal and not either teased or exhorted. Steve had talked to him like an equal, but that had been about history. Walter was talking about this strange family. As he got more worked up the red blotches on his neck seemed to stand out more than usual.

'Fred was very ill when he was thirteen and my wife, that is the strange thing, did not seem to care at all. She never showed him any affection. I had to sit with him and she just did not care. When we were still in Germany she was in a car crash with her mother, who had a heart attack and died there and then. There was a postmortem, and the coroner actually told my wife off because she was so indifferent. He asked why she showed no emotion. Do you know, the only time she told me she loved me was when she was about to leave me. We had had two children and she was about to go. She put her arms round me and said, "Walter, now I can feel that I love you." I ask you, is that normal?'

Walter looked at Karl and Karl did not know what to say, not being much of an expert on relationships with women. But his silence did not seem to upset Walter very much. He went on, his voice became sharper and there was an undertone of great tension in it.

'Of course I found out. She made one mistake. She had

126

gone on a little holiday. "I need a break, the bombing is getting me down." So I said I would look after everything, and then I got this postcard and it said, "We", yes, "*We* are having a wonderful time." It was the "we" that gave her away. Of course, the husband is always the last to know, that's a well known fact. But I began to wonder, who could it be? Of course it turned out to be the "best friend"; always hanging about, always being invited. I engaged a private detective and he got all the details. When she came home I told her to pack her bags. I told her, "Go and live with your accountant and see how you get on. No more little holidays, no more maid and house-keeper, just see how you get on." He is a professional man, an accountant. I thought they were supposed to have high principles. Of course, he is always putting ideas into her head. Now she wants her dowry back, the money her parents gave her when she married me. I told her, "You live in a cloud-cuckoo land, your money has gone. You have forgotten about Herr Hitler and running away from Germany." I mean, of course I got some money out. There were ways. You see that little Rembrandt etching; I had that remounted and put some dollars behind it. A very reliable man did it for me. She did not like that. "You and your money," she sneered. Well, now she wants it back. I told her she could have her bed and half the silver, her share of the furniture and whatever money she was genuinely entitled to. Of course, she is entitled to some money; but this rogue, this "best friend" he puts her up to it, and he doesn't deserve a penny. Money never meant much to her. She came from a very rich family. Does the name Dreher mean anything to you?'

Karl had to admit it did not.

'They were industrialists. Textiles, they began the textile industry in their part of the Austrian Empire before the first War. Made millions. Well, she grew up in a world where money was just there, you did not talk about it; you simply had it. Now this villain, this accountant, is after that money. He wants to squeeze every penny out of me. I must tell you, my solicitor – of course I had to take legal advice – laughed and said, "Levi, do you know, in a divorce case the biggest row is always over the soup ladle." "The soup ladle?" I asked. "Yes, it's the one thing that can't be split up." '

Walter laughed rather bitterly, then repeated the last line, as he usually did when he told an amusing story.

' "The one thing that can't be split up." And the children, the children always suffer. Not Hannah, she is tough, she just behaves as if nothing had happened, she can take it. But Fred, when Fred was ill, do you know what he said? "Dad, why don't you shoot him? Just bang, bang," and he made his fingers into a pistol: "Bang, bang." '

'I don't know,' thought Karl, 'that's not such an unreasonable reaction. Undesirable, yes, but why is Walter at such pains to make the boy sound as if he was not all there?'

But Walter went on, 'What I like about you is that you are manly, the boy needs a friend who will tell him about things.'

'*Nebbich*,' thought Karl. 'What do I know, two or three gropes in the woods at Elmfield. The only thing I have learnt is that girls' breasts are soft. Now I am supposed to be guide and advisor to this boy.'

Walter waved his hand dismissively, 'The boy is afraid of sex.'

'Who isn't?' thought Karl.

'At his age – but that's another story – at his age I certainly did not need any encouragement. My brother helped, of course. He gave me money once, so that I could go with a girl for the first time. "Here you are, Walter," he said, "time for a lesson." And he gave me a golden ten mark piece. God knows where he got it from. But Fred, when I said to him, "My boy, it's time you . . ." Do you know what he said? "Dad, what if I get one of those diseases?" I told him Salvarsan had been invented and in any case I would not mind if he got ill. Then there are precautions, you do not have to get caught.'

Karl wished he knew what they were. He, too, was afraid, and he rather admired Fred for his honesty. Precautions indeed. They had talked about it at length at school. Where would they get French letters from? The shame, the embarrassment; and then, what would you do when you had got them? 'Just think,' said Simon, 'you are with this girl and she is all for it and what do you do? Say, "Excuse me I must put this on"? Or, "Hang on a minute. I must just protect myself against the possibility of catching something nasty from you, and I certainly mustn't risk making you pregnant"?'

Walter carried on, unconscious of Karl's doubts and fears, because Karl was managing to look worldly and experienced, as if venereal disease did not frighten him at all. He could hear Ben. 'Lenin had it, Henry VIII had it, Richelieu had it, everyone had it.'

'I was sent to Frankfurt,' Walter went on, 'to learn the banking business. I suppose they would have sent you to Bleichroeder in Berlin if things had been different. Well, I was sent to the Frankfurt Warburgs. I had letters of introduction to all the best houses, but I made an interesting discovery. The manager of one House of Pleasure (that's what we called brothels) needed a book-keeper. After I had been visiting for a time – I think my poor mother would have died of shame – the madam made me a proposition: if I would do the books for her, I could have one of the girls whenever I felt like it. Why do you look so surprised, Karl? A brothel is a business and the books have to be kept up or else there is no order. And if there is no order money can't be made. They liked me, though. In those days I still had a good head of hair like yours; not fair, but a good head. I can remember the madam shouting down the corridor, "The little Jewboy is here." '

Walter looked thoughtfully at Karl. 'You have no idea how much money I spent on retaining my hair. I became bald unusually early and we tried everything, special treatments, vitamins, the lot. Now Karl, here is some money.' Karl was terrified; was he being given money to pay for a whore for himself and Fred? He glanced discreetly at his hand, and saw with relief that it was only a ten shilling note. Surely not enough for such adventures.

'Here you are. Take Fred into the West End and have some fun.'

Chapter 7

Karl was helping Frauelein von Seydlitz with the washing up. He did not feel sufficiently at ease with any of the Levi household to refuse. It was easy for the children to tell the Frauelein they were not going to help, he thought gloomily, but he was in a different position.

'Being a good boy, Karlchen?' Hannah asked. That was two hits in one go and Karl was impressed. She had not only spotted that he hated the diminutive 'Karlchen' which his sister plagued him with, but also realized that 'being a good boy' was not his ideal way of existing.

'Come on, you ate the meal as well, you could help a little bit,' grumbled the Frauelein bitterly. She seemed to find it very hard to speak to Hannah without sounding hostile or critical, but Hannah just gave her a long look and flounced out of the kitchen. The Frauelein was cross.

'I really don't see why you should be made to do all the housework. The children never help unless I make a scene, and I can't go on nagging. I wish Mr Levi would just occasionally tell that brat that she is not living in a hotel. I sometimes think he does not realize that without me the household would completely collapse.'

Karl thought that on the contrary Walter Levi was most probably well aware of her importance, especially now that his wife had left. Indeed, he had said to Karl, 'The Frauelein really is marvellous; she has stuck to the family through thick and thin. She knew all about the goings on when my wife was having an affair, and was terribly upset. She came to me

130

with tears in her eyes. "Mr Levi, I am so glad you have found out, I could not stand the deception any longer." And I believed her. If I had thought she was disloyal I would have thrown her out there and then.'

He said this in such a way that Karl feared he, too, would be thrown out without further ado if he failed to come up to expectation in any way. That was partly why he helped to wash up, cut the lawn and make himself as useful as he could; it was his way of preserving his separate entity. It might look like bootlicking, but to Karl it was a way of paying his way. Frauelein von Seydlitz went on with her tale of woe while she wiped soapsuds off the plates.

'You just can't imagine what it was like, the tension and the misery. I had to keep everything together. But Mr Levi is a marvellous man, so generous, you cannot imagine how many people he has helped. Once I said to him, "We might as well call this house Victoria Station." Everyone came through, and there was always a meal and always a bed. He has been so good to me, too, though I am not even Jewish.'

Karl had never doubted that. Her name, her steely blue eyes and her way of moving, the very way she talked, gave away her origins. She would never have been taken for a Jew.

The Frauelein went on, 'You see I worked for Mr Levi in Germany, in the Bank, and I was disgusted by what was happening. It was filthy and unfair, it made me ashamed to be a German. When Mr Levi told me he was leaving I asked him if he would take me with him. I told him I would do anything that would help him, and he asked me to be his housekeeper. And that is what I am. Like most refugees, I am doing things now that I never dreamt I would have to do – but it is better than being in Germany. There was nothing there to keep me. My sister is still there, but I think she might have left, too, if it had not been for her family.'

Karl was moved and impressed. After all, neither he nor his sister nor the Levis had any real choice. They either left or else – he was not sure what the 'else' was, but it seemed certain that things were going badly for the people who had stayed behind. That had been clear even before the war started, when warnings to leave Germany were constantly given, particularly to people who had had a spell in a concentration camp already. But the Frauelein was a 'pure' German, so for her it was a deliberate decision. She had come out on the side of the hated and despised Jews, and was not finding life as a housekeeper easy.

'So, here I am doing the dishes, and nagging an obstreperous adolescent. That Hannah is a little beast, and her proud father just sits back and enjoys the insults she throws at me. The other day, for instance, we were having coffee after lunch, as we always do, and Hannah turned to her father and said, "Dad, I wish you would buy some decent cigarettes for that box. Frauelein von Seydlitz does not like the brand you keep there." I suppose one ought to be impressed by her cunning. With one blow she succeeded in suggesting that her father is mean *and* that I steal the family's cigarettes. I smoke a lot but I have never, never, taken a cigarette except when it is offered. I don't know why, but I cannot seem to establish a good relationship with that girl. Perhaps it is her age. Perhaps I am just not very good with young people, too old and set in my ways. Hannah, of course, would say that it is because I am a Prussian. Oh, yes, don't look surprised, I often get that thrown at me. Of course, I am not a perfect housekeeper, I had to learn. I was a top level private secretary, doing all the confidential work of the Bank. I had the widest possible power to use my own discretion and act independently. I was encouraged to make decisions on Mr Levi's behalf. And now, now I worry because the gardener is eating all our onions – he eats them raw, you know!'

One Sunday, after lunch, Walter explained to Karl, 'A visitor is coming this afternoon who would like to meet you. His name is Werner Werthal, and he is an old friend of the family's who knew your father. So I have asked Margot as well. He is a real *nebbich*, but he has had a hard time. He came from a very distinguished, rich family. You should have seen the entertainments they laid on. I remember my father saying, "It's too much; an ostentatious display of wealth is dangerous. It attracts attention and leads to anti-semitism." But that meant

132

nothing to the Werthals. Everyone in Berlin came to their parties, no anti-semitism then, all they wanted to do was gobble up the caviar. And yet, and that is the odd thing about people as rich as that, they were extraordinarily mean. Old Mrs Werthal, later Frau Geheimrat Werthal, used to buy lavatory paper wholesale because it was cheaper. Well, there is nothing wrong with that, but the quality! It still had woodshavings in it and it was dangerous. You could easily find a splinter stuck in your behind. And she collected small bits of soap ends and stuck them together. Of course, now, in the war, we all do it.'

Karl had noticed that each piece of soap in the house had a little metal stud stuck into it, the sort you put into heels of shoes to stop them wearing out too quickly. The stud apparently prevented the soap from lying in a pool of water and dissolving.

'Werner's father was a nasty piece of work if there ever was one. A capitalist of the worst sort. I mean, I've nothing against making money, but I don't see the need to exploit and destroy as he did. He said to me once, "Levi, I never look at a factory I buy, I don't want to know the people in case I have to close it down; and if I know the people I might regret what has to be done. When you are stripping the assets you don't want to be emotionally involved. They have a phrase for it in England: "business is business."'

'And pigs is pigs,' thought Karl.

Walter sensed his doubt, 'You may be surprised to hear this, but when I was a young man I had very advanced ideas. I was critical of my father's dealings. During the Revolution of 1918, I was stationed in Berlin before coming out of the army. I was elected to represent the soldiers on the council, and my father was mad with rage. "What do you think you are doing, representing the communists, that rabble. Keep your head down and stay out of sight. No good will come of all this, mark my words. I don't want you mixed up with it." Of course he was right, it was a bit odd; a member of the Levi Bank representing the soldiers. And it did end badly, look what happened to Liebknecht and Rosa Luxemburg. I certainly had no wish to end up like them, face down in the Landwehrkanal.

'To come back to Werner, he works in a Lyons Corner House now, doing the books. They have been really good to refugees, you know, any number of them found jobs there. Not very marvellous jobs, but paying enough to survive on during the first difficult time. I was lucky, I got enough money out to be able to sit back and survey the scene until I saw what could be done. But Werner had to get straight out and work. He behaves as if he is the senior accountant there so as to hide his humiliation. Let him, poor devil, I say. Without the family bank to prop him up he will never be any good. I would not let him manage the local bank here, let alone a big branch. Not that the English manager of the bank I use here is any good. If he was working for me I would have sacked him years ago. Fool. Not that it matters, I tell him what to do and he is grateful. By the way, Karl, never go to your bank manager for financial advice. They are small men and all they do is sell you bits and pieces of information they get from the papers, and gossip. They have no overall view of the financial situation.'

Karl promised himself that he would never go to a bank manager for financial advice. He felt as if one great financier had been talking to another. He would have liked to carry on the conversation, and ask if his Post Office Savings book was a safe repository for the fourteen pounds he'd saved, but had no chance as Werner arrived dead on time, a quarter to four. He was immaculately dressed. Not a speck of dust on his coat, and his trousers were beautifully pressed. He wore a big pearl in the middle of his heavy silk tie and his cufflinks had small diamonds sparkling in them. He looked pale and drawn. His eyes were red and fishlike, and his mouth was drawn down at the corners. He had very little chin.

'Hullo, Levi, am I here on time? As they say, punctuality is the courtesy of princes. How are you, how is the furniture polish?'

Karl did not like him, his over-formal manner, his foppish dress or his rather droll, old-fashioned German. 'So this is the scion of capitalist Berlin,' Karl thought. Walter Levi introduced him to Werner.

'This is Karl, the Hartland boy; his sister will be here any minute now. You know the Hartlands, of course.'

'Oh, yes, I had the pleasure of meeting your dear father on many occasions.'

Margot came into the room. She had made a special effort and was wearing her grey costume and real stockings, not the usual dye that she put on her legs. Werthal jumped to attention, though he did not actually click his heels as Karl hoped he would; but he held Margot's hand for a long time. Karl looked across to Hannah who was about to giggle.

Werthal spoke, still holding Margot's hand. 'Delighted to meet you, Frauelein Hartland, an honour to meet a member of your family. I trust you are well.'

Karl was disgusted. 'The old goat fancies her. Her, of all people!' While he could see that his sister was well turned out, he found it difficult to understand that anyone might find her attractive. Margot's manner had changed since Karl's first visit to the Levi's house, he noticed. She seemed more at ease now, more confident.

Walter kept the conversation going. He was like the conductor as well as the principal soloist. It was not easy for anyone to get a word in unless actually encouraged by him to do so. 'Dear Werner, you asked how the furniture polish is going. Well I am pleased to tell you it's a success story. If only we could get more raw materials from the Ministry we could cover the country with furniture polish. Gruesome stuff, by the way, never buy it! I would not dream of putting it on my Sheraton table top, it would ruin the wood.'

As Werner Werthal put out a hand for his cup of coffee, Karl noticed that the cuff of his shirt was slightly frayed. The loose bits of thread had been trimmed. Werner turned to Frauelein von Seydlitz, who handed the cups round but then sat down behind the circle of family and guests.

'Ah, it's a delicious cup of coffee that you make, Frauelein; this is one of the few houses where one still gets a decent cup of coffee. The coffee in England! I know the English have great qualities but their coffee . . .'

This was always a safe topic, something on which everyone

could agree. Only Karl did not want to agree. 'The people I stayed with made excellent coffee.'

The honour of all his friends at Elmfield seemed at stake. He did not want to be part of these museum pieces, living in a world of their own. But no one took much notice of his remark, and Walter directed the conversation towards Berlin.

'You will, of course, remember the meeting with Bleichroeder, that was in '29, no, '30, before those bandits got in. It must have been '30, because it was before the Landesmann merger.'

Werner was deferential, 'Was that not the meeting when you flew in in your special plane?'

Walter explained to Karl and Margot. 'Yes. I was stuck in Hamburg. No train to get me back in time and they were important negotiations. So I had a brainwave. I hired a plane and a pilot and got to the negotiating table dead on time. They were not expecting me, and of course it did no harm, casually mentioning that I had just flown in. I still remember the thick leather coat and goggles the hire firm lent me.'

Werner seemed gratified that he was in the presence of such an important man. He sighed. 'Yes, those were the days . . .'

Hannah was interested. 'Were you sick in the plane? You always puke when you are on a ship.'

Frauelein von Seydlitz said sharply, 'Really, Hannah, you will spoil our appetites. Your father is never sea-sick, you are just making it up, trying to make him look silly.'

Walter went on, quite undeterred. 'We had just moved into our house at the Tiergarten. Does that place mean anything to you, Karl?'

Margot broke in. 'No, the poor lad had never been to Berlin, he would have no idea that that is the best part of town.'

Karl felt himself blushing. How she always managed to chip in and keep him down, poor provincial that he was. He remembered feeling very jealous when she went to Berlin on her own to learn fashion design. She always acted in a slightly superior manner, just because she had had a couple of years in the great capital. 'How they all live in the past,' Karl thought. 'They need each other to demonstrate their importance now that they are nothing. Walter needs Werner, even though he lives in better circumstances. Without Werner we might not believe that he was once a great financier, that's why he's so nice to that fishfaced twat.'

Walter was still talking. 'Yes, it was a good part of the town. Do you know, when we left we sold the house to the British Consul – even then we had close connections with this country. We were on visiting terms with him. Of course, it was still all very formal then, visiting cards and a butler. Don't you think, Werthal, it is a good thing that we are free from that conventional, stuffy approach to life?'

Werner thought not, 'No, no, not at all. You knew where you were then, you knew whom to receive and to whom you were not at home. I hate all this democratic rubbish; everyone thinking they are equal. Well, believe me they are not.'

Karl was very angry. That was just the sort of attitude he was growing to hate.

'I thought this war was all about democracy and equality,' he insisted. 'To make opportunities available to everyone. After all if you expect people to die in a war, you must also offer them some degree of equality as a reward for their sacrifices.'

Werthal did not want an argument with this tiresome boy. He stared at him with his wet, fishy eyes. 'Yes, democracy. Oh, yes, to be sure, democracy. But look at the achievements of the societies that were not democratic, the beauty of Renaissance painting or the gardens of Versailles.'

Karl was about to protest that thousands of labourers died of malaria laying out the gardens at Versailles, when Walter intervened, changed the subject and took the heat out of the occasion. Karl, however, was pleased to see that Hannah had enjoyed his attack on Fishface. She had told him earlier.

'He is a terrible man. We played bridge one evening and I won, I usually do, but you should have seen old Werthal. He went red and spluttered and said something about it being too bad that a child should spend so much time at cards that she was better than adults. Do you know something? He has a girl-friend! Can you imagine, a girlfriend. She'd need a hot water bottle as well as him to keep her warm.'

Walter turned to Karl. 'Let me tell you how formality worked in so-called good society before the War. First a letter of introduction was needed. Then you had to call, leaving a visiting card; and it had to be the right sort of card, mind.'

Werthal was not going to be left out. 'Yes, I always ran my finger over the card. If it was not printed with a die it was not worth having. You could feel the slight ridge.'

For once Hannah volunteered to help wash the crockery after lunch, and Karl followed her into the kitchen. They both began to laugh. Hannah said, 'Look out for Werthal, he is after your sister, the old goat.'

'I thought he had a girlfriend.'

'Ah, but he'd like to get off with a Hartland. He probably thinks you are still rich. After all, Margot does look quite posh, tailored jacket and little fur collar.'

Karl thought about that. When he and Hannah went back into the drawing room his sister was lighting a cigarette. Werthal had already jumped up and was fiddling with a book of matches, but before he had even torn out a match Margot had lit her cigarette. Karl looked at the lighter. She had never had a lighter before, and furthermore, he had recently seen a lighter exactly like it on Walter's desk. He wondered who was after whom. After all, he said to himself, it's only a lighter. But it wasn't only the lighter. It was the change in his sister, and the way Walter was taking such great trouble over him. Karl felt slightly ill.

'He doesn't give a damn for me,' he fumed. 'All this talk! He is just trying to make a good impression, buttering me up so that I can't object if he has an affair with Margot. On the other hand, what has it got to do with me? My sister doesn't interfere with my life. On the contrary she has really helped me. She annoys me but she has looked after me. In any case what is so awful about Walter? I teased her months ago and said, "How about Mr Levi? You fancy older men, don't you?" She got so cross, I thought perhaps I wasn't so far off the truth.'

Karl wondered what he ought to do. He felt used and betrayed, but at the same time quite pleased. 'He won't throw me out now, he can't. Egg spread for the rest of my life and a good room.' Then he felt miserable, as if he had lost some-

138

thing. His freedom, perhaps. He had no wish to become part of this set-up he dreaded so much. The family was closing in on him again. If he weren't careful, he could easily become a Frauelein von Seydlitz, a sort of superior retainer, allowed to have coffee with the boss after lunch, but who had to be loyal and mind his p's and q's. Perhaps that would be a more honest stance than just pretending nothing was happening.

Karl made a decision. On Monday he would go to the nearest recruiting office. The sooner he could get into the army the better. He did not want to sit for the next scholarship exam. He would pretend he was going to, or else they might not let him stay; but he wanted to get out and to be free. He did not have to spend his afternoons in the local library if he didn't want to. He hated the smell of the floor polish there but he went because he felt he had to get out of the house sometimes. Karl was reading about the Thirty Years War; at least, he was putting his head down and making notes occasionally. Sometimes it seemed to him that by the time he had finished he would have more notes than there were pages in the book.

Walter was pleased with Karl. 'I wish my children would work as hard as you do. But here everything gets taken for granted. For them it is just a joke, I pay through the nose for their education, and they sit around doing nothing except complain.'

Hannah was cross, when she heard this. 'I don't cost you very much,' she grumbled. 'You send *me* to that crummy grammar school. It's Fred who has to be paid for, not me. But then girls' education isn't important, is it? You should be delighted to have such a cheap daughter. You can save money and buy even more black market food to hoard.'

She turned to Karl. 'By the way, I must show you the cupboard he hoards all the food in. It's illegal, of course, but that does not worry my father. You crook, you hoarder. Do you know one of the tins of ham blew up last week. It had been kept for so long it just blew up. He could not bear to open it and give it to anyone. It was real justice that it blew up, except for the mess it made, but then he didn't have to clean that up, either. Someone else did that.'

That did it. Walter turned on Hannah, purple in the face with rage. 'Mess, who are you to accuse me of making a mess? Have you tidied up that pigsty we call your room?'

He looked at Karl and shrugged, trying to control his temper and obviously anxious to make light of this hoarding business.

'That's an old one about hoarding food. When the war broke out, you know, they asked us to keep ourselves supplied for emergencies. Then suddenly it became illegal. I have lived through the First War when there was real famine, and I am not taking any chances this time.'

Then Walter turned to Hannah again, his voice quite different, sharp, hostile. 'You haven't told me yet when you are going to tidy your room. Well?'

Hannah sounded cheerful, as if she hadn't a care in the world. 'Later, Dad.'

'Not later, now. Now, I say. I am sick and tired of hearing complaints about your room. This morning Frauelein von Seydlitz said to me, "I don't know how she can live in a mess like that, it is frightful," and she is right. Now come on, go and tidy that room.'

Hannah was still trying to sound reasonable. 'Don't *nag*, Dad. Anyhow it's my room and I don't know what all the fuss is about. It doesn't smell and the untidiness doesn't worry me. You don't have to go in there if you don't want to.'

Walter was beside himself. Karl was quite frightened at the sight of this urbane and polished man in such a rage. 'What do you mean "*my* room"? This is *my* house and I have the right to demand a decent standard. If you can't accept my standards, get out. Go on, get out of *my* house. You are impossible, you annoy everyone, you don't accept any responsibility for the housework. Do you know something? You are a slut! Go on, get out, if you can't behave like a reasonable human being.'

Hannah was angry but by no means subdued. The row had moved beyond the issue of the room by now and Hannah's mother came into the quarrel.

'That's right, throw me out! Throwing people out is what

you're good at, isn't it?' she goaded. 'That's the only way you know how to act. You are a dictator. Everyone has to obey you, you bloody dictator.'

Walter seemed to have forgotten Karl, who was standing aside from this very embarrassing scene, not quite sure what was the right thing to say, and very much aware of the red blotches which had appeared on Walter's neck. Walter suddenly realized Karl was still there, and turned to him for support.

'What do you think, Karl? Am I being unreasonable? Is it too much to ask one's daughter to keep her room tidy. I bet you would not want to live in a sty like that.'

Karl was uncertain. As he was not only not in his own house, but also using someone else's room, he was very conscious of being in a position where he had to be exceedingly tidy. But he did not like too much tidiness, and often wished he could be himself and just throw things wherever he pleased. Then his sympathies were entirely with Hannah. It seemed to him that both Walter and the Frauelein were always nagging her. She seemed unable to please either of them, and of course made it worse by her jokes and her mockery. So Karl grunted in an uncommitted sort of way which did not please Walter.

'Let me tell you a story, Karl, you may see the point. There was this *Yeshiva bocher*, know what that is? Well, it is a sort of Talmudic scholar, a poor young boy apprenticed to a Rabbi. Well, the rabbi and his wife got fed up with the boy and wanted to be rid of him, so they made a plan. The Rabbi said, "Tomorrow at lunch I'll say the soup is too salty and you say, "no, it isn't", and then we will ask the *bocher* what he thinks. If he agrees with you *I'll* throw him out, and if he agrees with me *you* insist that he goes." They carried out their plan at lunch the next day, but when they asked the *bocher* to give his verdict all he said was, "For the remaining three years of my stay with you, I am determined not to fall out with either of you." '

Karl saw the point all right. Walter had made it clear that he knew what he was up to, and wanted him to be on his side. Walter laughed heartily at his story, and Karl decided his best plan was also to treat the whole thing as a good joke.

Later in the evening, when Karl was already in bed, the row flared up again. He heard Hannah shrieking, 'Get out of my room, you pig. Look what you have done, you bastard, you blackmarketeering bastard, you dictator!'

Walter shouted back, and there was no refined control in his voice this time. 'I warned you, I warned you, and now I have done what I said I would do. If you want to live in a room like a pigsty I'll make sure it is a proper one.'

Walter was shouting in German, and Hannah was shouting back at him in English.

'Just look at my things. How dare you tip everything into the middle of the room. It's all in a mess. You bully, you pig!'

The shouting and shrieking went on a bit longer. It was obvious to Karl that Walter had tipped all Hannah's belongings on to her bedroom floor. He wondered if he ought to come out of his room and try to act as a mediator, but before he had made any sort of decision both of them had retreated. The doors of each room were slammed loudly, as if to say, 'Well, this is where I am if you want me.'

Karl was not used to family rows. In the approved school camp, and at Elmfield there had been rows and fights but this was different. This was family. Because he had been without a family now for four years, Karl had built up an idealized picture. Nevertheless, he had to admit to himself that his re-entry into family life at the Levis filled him with a sense of claustrophobia and horror. They did not seem able to make each other happy in any way. They managed to survive from day to day by the exercise of a certain formal politeness, and even, when the occasion demanded, being quite pleasant to each other. Then suddenly all the veneer would crack.

The day after the row Walter took Karl for a walk in the garden.

'What do you think of last night's little drama?' he asked.

Karl wondered. Was Walter trying to get him on his side or was he merely embarrassed that they had behaved so badly in front of a visitor. Walter was quite calm and controlled now. That was another thing that amazed Karl about families; the incredible anger and aggression could vanish in a moment, and

142

then all would be well again. Except that in this family all was not well. The mother had left, the father was having an affair with Karl's sister and they were all distantly related.

Walter went on. 'Do you know what the real problem is? I was thinking last night, and some of my discussions with my psychiatrist came back to me. I have been seeing Loewenberg, you know, a top man. I had to when I needed advice over the divorce. He has helped me a lot.'

Karl was impressed. Walter seemed to be able to buy whatever help he needed. 'I suppose,' Karl thought, 'that is what happens when you are rich. You can command the services of doctors, lawyers, accountants or whoever you need at the time. Then it's not difficult to appear all wise and knowledgeable. I wonder if he buys his little jokes and anecdotes wholesale.'

Walter interrupted his thoughts. 'Well, Loewenberg told me a few home truths. I think I told you his opinion of my wife's poetry. He said, "Of course, you are right, her development is retarded. She is acting out her adolescence, and refuses to take the full responsibility of family life." Now I fear the same thing will happen with Hannah, that is why I am so worried. She is so like her mother – '

Karl again found his thoughts questioning Walter's attitude. 'Well, that's not her fault, is it? After all, she *is* an adolescent and she's untidy. What's so bad about that? But then I suppose people have been shot for less.'

'– She is so like her mother, a slut if ever there was one. I want the girl to grow up with some decent standards. Is that so wrong? Here am I doing my best, and what do I get in return? I am called a blackmarketeer and a fascist bastard. That's one thing about my daughter, she is never short of the apt phrase when it comes to abuse.'

Karl would have liked to say, 'Neither are you,' but he decided it would be safer to keep quiet.

'It's true, I do have a number of tins in the dining room cupboard, and your aunt Eunice sends parcels regularly. Am I to throw the contents away? And I do come home with the odd egg or some coffee – people in the factory are always pleased to swap things, and they get hold of extra meat and so on from undisclosed sources. I am not going to report my own workers to the Ministry of Food. And I'll tell you another thing, not one of the little idealists in this house has ever refused to eat the eggs or the meat that I have obtained.'

Karl was even more sure why Walter talked to him like this. 'It's because of Margot,' he thought. 'He wants to make a good impression on me, because, if I were to tell her what an out-and-out bastard he is to his own daughter, it might put her off.'

Walter remained happily ignorant of Karl's disloyal thoughts. In fact, he was warming to his theme. 'It is too bad, the little beast manages to upset everyone. Now it is Frauelein von Seydlitz. You know what she is like, absolute integrity personified, and when she says something she means it. Of course, she is a bit strict and not the most humorous of people but I admire her, and she has stuck to the family through thick and thin. I always think she would have made a good drill sergeant. Have you noticed how she walks? I always wonder if she doesn't have a walking stick stuck up her back. Well, she said to me, and I must listen to her, you understand, humour her, or else who would look after the house while I am at the factory. "Mr Levi," she said, "how can I keep a reasonably clean and tidy house when that brat fouls up everything. And she won't help at all, you know. It's not right that a girl of her age should not help a bit. If only she kept her own room in order, that would be something." You must understand we owe a lot to the Frauelein. It was not easy for her to say to me, "May I come with you, I can't stand this Nazi nonsense." When she went for her permit to leave Germany one of the officials said, "Why are you shacking up with a Jew family? Where is your loyalty to the Reich?" She must have been very brave to stick to her guns. It wasn't beyond those bastards to accuse her of having an illegal relationship with me, and that was a serious crime, you know.'

Walter smiled at the absurdity of the notion that he might have had such a relationship with her, but Karl wondered whether her unlimited devotion to the family was based entirely on a political point of view. 'It will be interesting to see how

144

she will take to the news that there are "goings-on" with my sister,' he thought, and wondered if there would be another splendid row. Walter returned to the psychiatrist, who seemed to have had the knack of explaining away every problem.

'Now, Doctor Loewenberg, he explained to me how the girl is torn between two forces – me and her mother. And I make matters worse, you see, because I am haunted by the fear that she will become like her mother. I have had enough of untidy sluts around me. I want her tidy and methodical, and so does Frauelein von Seydlitz. Are we wrong?'

No, Karl did not think there was anything wrong with that, but he did wonder if it was fair to act out a marital row and make Hannah a pawn in it.

'Perhaps,' Karl ventured cautiously, 'Hannah needs to show some loyalty to her mother, and that is the way she does it. She imitates her to show that she is part of her.'

It interested Karl to see how the 'heredity factor' always came up when he did something that his sister did not approve of, usually over money. At home, when his school work had been poor, he had been told that he was just like his Uncle Eric. Now it was extravagance that apparently ran through the non-banking part of the family like some ravaging disease.

'It's my money, for God's sake,' Karl raged. 'I earned it teaching Canadians German, not that it did them much good; most of them were killed or taken prisoner on the Dieppe raid. Then there was an old lady whose lawn I cut; she paid me. Then if I spent the money I earned on the farm, well that was little enough, anyhow. It's a good thing for me I'm going to be independent soon.'

He had talked to Alice about going into the Army. 'Well,' she said, 'why not? You can't go on being at school for ever. Learning is a marvellous thing, but it's no substitute for common sense. As my father, may God rest him in peace, once said of the learned professor next door to us, "When he buys a house, the *mezzuseh* alone will bankrupt him." Do you still know what they are?'

Karl noticed, with a mixture of pleasure and annoyance, that whenever the family used a Jewish expression they would considerately offer to interpret it for him. 'Do you know what they are?' 'Do you know what that means?' It was obvious they sensed how his 'Jewishness' was leaving him, and in a strange way admired him for it. Well, their attitude was worth exploiting. 'Go on, Mr Soldier,' he thought, 'have some more chicken – you won't get that in the army.'

Karl received a letter from the Army: he must report to the Euston Road Recruiting Office if he wished to be considered as a volunteer. At last! Karl was elated. No more having to pretend to be working for the examination, no more family rows, no more worries.

The recruiting sergeant looked up when he had read Karl's filled in application form. 'Christ,' he said, 'another Jerry. I've had several of your sort lately. Why don't you join the Jerry Army? This is getting to be like the Foreign Legion. Hey! Would you like to join that, and try to forget the woman who betrayed you?'

Karl was cross, 'Here we go again. What eagerness to win the war! They can't even be bothered to recruit men who want to fight, and they're a long way from winning yet.'

But he realized the sergeant was not all that serious; that was one of the problems with the English. They were often joking when they looked quite serious; they teased, and if one did not respond to the teasing they would accuse one of not having a sense of humour. And nothing, but nothing, was worse than not having their sense of humour, except perhaps not to be too keen on games. So Karl joined in the game.

'Haven't got a woman to forget; all alone.'

'Never mind, son, once you get in the Army they'll be crowding round you.'

Karl felt quite hopeful. Perhaps it was true, if only it was true. Vanessa had said, 'Oh, Karl, you will be irresistible in uniform.' But then she added, 'Just don't become too carried away with all that patriotism – remember E. M. Forster: "If I had to choose between my friends and my country, I hope I would have the courage to choose my friends." '

146

The sergeant seemed quite pleased now. 'Well, my son, what mob would you like to volunteer for?'

Karl remembered the rousing talk by the officer at school and asked for the Tank Corps. He thought it would be quite straightforward, and that the sergeant would merely say, 'Right, Tank Corps. Second door on the left.' and that he would emerge in a few hours, looking 'devastating' in a black beret.

Instead the sergeant said, 'Sorry mate, not recruiting for the Tank Corps at the moment.'

'But a few months ago an officer came to my school and said they badly needed people.'

'Yeah, well, a few months ago; but it's different now. Anyhow what's wrong with the Infantry? All I know is we are recruiting for the PBI now. Don't look so sad, son, we can't all be with the glamour boys. Infantry is all right, queen of the battlefield, couldn't do without the Infantry – right, go through there for your medical.'

After the medical Karl was given seven shillings and six pence, swore an oath of allegiance and then was told, 'We'll let you know where to report. It will take a few weeks.'

Karl wished it had been immediately; but everything at home suddenly became unimportant, and it didn't seem long before he was told to go to Glasgow to report to the Highland Light Infantry.

The evening before Karl was to go Walter took him aside. 'Let me say one thing, Karl. I know you are a very idealistic person and I respect that, the young don't approve of the black market, they want to fight for democracy and I am sure that is right. But remember what happened to my brother, a great hero and then suddenly – paff – a corpse. Don't ever volunteer for anything dangerous. It's easy to be carried away, but just stay in the background. In the army it isn't done to push oneself to the front. I ought to know. After all, I served in his Imperial Majesty's Balloon Corps in the last war. They were quite decent when they called me up. It was rumoured that the authorities were willing to do their best to see that one son in a family survived, and there wasn't much danger in the balloon corps. But if I *had* done something dangerous, who would thank me today? I think what happened in any case was that my father, must have gone to the authorities and said, "Look, one of my sons has been killed already. Who is to carry on the business when I am gone, and I am an old man now." He may of course have greased a few palms. Anyhow I ended up with the balloons in France. I must tell you, though, I did get into trouble once, because of a pair of boots. The boots they issued in the Prussian army were quite dreadful. I could hardly stand up in them, and within days my feet were dreadfully blistered. The quartermaster said, "What are you complaining of? Your feet will fit the boots in the end." On my first leave I went to my own bootmaker and had a pair of boots made specially. They were designed to look like army boots, but they were made of the best English leather. I said to him, "They must look rough, like army issue boots." Anyhow, the point of the story is this: my sergeant spotted them. I don't think there is anything worse in the world than a Prussian regular drill sergeant. "Who the hell do you think you are, you little Jewboy?" he shouted. "Little Lord Fauntleroy? What do you think this is, the royal ballet? I'll kick you up the arse until your teeth begin to shake." The army vocabulary was choice. In the end I slipped him a twenty mark piece. He calmed down and my feet survived the war. Every man has his price, you see.'

Walter took Karl's arm and they walked on. 'Now, Karl, this is entirely "entre nous", but I think you should know. Margot and I are planning to get married.'

As Karl had already noticed something was going on he was not bowled over with surprise. Nor did he know what was the right thing to say. Should it be, 'So glad you are making an honest woman of my poor, violated sister,' or 'How nice for you to have found a willing young bit of crumpet.' He also wanted to tell Walter what he thought of his treatment of him. 'I know that's why you have been so friendly to me. As you just said, every man has his price. Mine is a spare bed and a really good meal now and again.'

But all he said was, 'I am so pleased. Of course, I am not surprised. I knew something was going on, I spotted Margot

148

using the lighter some weeks ago.' He made this last remark because he didn't see why they should get away with thinking that they had pulled the wool over his eyes.

'I hope you will be very happy together. It seemed to me that you would be a suitable match the first time we met!'

Walter's voice became even more confidential. 'I would rather you did not mention our engagement to anyone. There are problems – Hannah, as you know, is going to a boarding school and I don't want her to feel she is being pushed out of her home. Then there is Fred. I never know what he is thinking. And there is the Frauelein; I am not sure, but there may be some difficulty there; I wonder if perhaps she had hoped to be the lady of the house one day. I do remember once, when she was washing my underpants, she said with a prophetic ring in her voice, "Mr Levi, if you ever marry some young chit, one thing you can be sure of, she won't wash your underpants!" And my mother, she thinks all women I like are loose hussies after my money, so she needs to be prepared carefully for the new state of affairs, and we must proceed cautiously. You, Karl, are the first to know and I know you will be discreet and diplomatic.'

Walter produced a small package. 'A small gift, a sort of engagement present. To show how pleased I am that you are now almost one of the family.'

It occurred to Karl that he would be Hannah's uncle. This was going to be tricky, and he was glad he was about to escape any further family conflicts. He had been told to report to the Maryhill barracks in Glasgow the next day. On the all-night train journey, Karl sat opposite a huge sailor who had letters tattooed on his fingers. The left hand read 'Fuck'; and the right 'Love'.

Chapter 8

Karl had become Hannam in the army, not Hartland; and had changed his first name from Karl to Charles. The captain had called Karl into the tent. 'We have to change your name; with a name like yours the Germans will shoot you if they take you prisoner. What do you want to change it to?'

Karl had stood to attention and thought feverishly. He already had a number, and everything they gave him had the number on it. Then had come the matter of issuing him with an identity disc.

'Name?' asked the soldier who was stamping the discs. 'Christ, another bleeding foreign name; how do you spell it, mate? Religion?'

This is the moment, Karl thought, to shed my religion. I can be rid of it, I am sick and tired of being asked about and labelled with a religion I do not believe in. I don't believe in God (that maniacal rugger player, if he exists at all, Vanessa had said). So he answered 'Leave it blank, please, no religion.'

'Can't do that,' said the soldier, 'you've got to have a religion on these discs.'

'Can't you leave it blank?'

'No, mate, can't do that. Tell you what, I'll put C of E on it.'

That was too much for Karl, leaving it blank was one thing, but to be Church of England – he thought of the Vicar at Elmfield, thanking God for his mercy and for the success of the thousand bomber raid. No, he wouldn't be C of E. He

150

was forsaking the religion of his fathers. 'If I forget thee, oh Jerusalem . . .' Surely lightning would strike him.

A corporal came up. 'What's the trouble?'

'It's this bloke, Corp, can't make up his mind what his religion is. Wants me to leave his discs blank.'

'What's the matter with you?' asked the corporal crossly, 'Don't you even know what your religion is?'

Karl wanted to know why it mattered all that much. Why should his religion go on those green and dark brown plastic discs.

'It's for when they bury you, your bloody funeral. One disc is fireproof, the other rotproof. That's why you've got two discs. Now, for God's sake get a move on, there's the rest of the platoon to do.'

'Go on,' Karl pleaded, 'it doesn't matter to you, does it? Leave it blank. You don't have to bury me, that's some other poor sod's problem.'

'All right, here you are.'

Karl was pleased with his blank disc. He would have liked 'agnostic' on it, but he decided he had exhausted all the good will that was to be had at that moment. He felt that the discs had given him a new identity, and he was happy.

Then, suddenly, he had been asked to change his name. All sorts of names raced through his mind: Hamilton – no, Harris – no, too tweedy, and then: Hannam, the quiltmaker who had bequeathed his fortune to the Elmfield village school in the eighteenth century. Yes, a suitable tribute to the school which had set Karl on the road to being a new man, had taught him English so well that people only took notice when he mentioned his name, had got him a place at university and enabled him to put 'student' under 'profession' in his paybook.

And now his time in the army was nearly over. Karl was due for demobilization. He thought, 'I am still alive, and that's nice. But leaving the army? I don't know. Everyone else was always moaning, but was it as bad as all that? It's the longest I have ever been with any group, *and* they made me a sergeant *and* I have got a row of medal ribbons, which really do look rather smart.'

On the last evening before demobilization an officer came round. 'Well, men, anyone signing on? Five years? Seven years? I'll tell you one thing, civvy street isn't all that lovely. A skilled soldier like any one of you is needed here. Join the Indian Army, and I guarantee you will be at least a captain within three years. They need white specialists.'

'Too true,' muttered private Innell, 'them fucking wogs, couldn't organize two budgies in a cage. I would stay on but they won't have me, not with my record. It's a bleeding shame, I was a mortar sergeant and then I went and hit that bloke and they busted me.'

Karl had served with Innell for a long time. They met first when Karl was posted to the Royal Midlands. He was huge, and everyone was afraid of him. He took to Karl, who was not in any position of authority, and it pleased the big man to look after him.

'Come on, Charlie, give us your pack,' he had said once. They were on an island off the coast of Burma. The company was assembled. Major Taylor 'addressed' the men – he never 'spoke'. There was always a suppressed note of hysteria in his voice.

'I want to put you men into the picture.'

'Here we go to the fucking pictures again,' Innell muttered, and Karl nearly burst out laughing. That was the trouble. Innell was incredibly funny, but it was a pity the major saw Karl laughing.

He had detested Karl ever since he had found out that he had rather a good academic record. Taylor obviously disliked the idea of a private being intelligent, and he said to Karl, 'Well, I failed my school certificate, but I have got further than you, so don't think you are all that clever.'

The major liked to imagine he was Montgomery; so he spent a lot of time 'putting the men in the picture.'

'You are laughing. There is nothing to laugh about where you're going.' For just a moment he screeched, but then his voice became clipped and controlled again.

'We are on our way to Rangoon, and we are going to hit the Jap hard. This will be a big operation; paratroops, the

Gurkhas, combined ops, and I am proud to be leading this company, the best of the Royal Midlands, into action. It's going to be tough, and I am glad. You have had it soft for too long.'

'Hark at him,' Innell whispered. 'Old petrol feet. He's never been out of a jeep in his life. Listen, when we were in Calcutta – the Calcutta Homeguard, they called us – half the battalion went down with VD, and so did he, the dirty bastard!'

Major Taylor went on, 'We are marching to the embarkation area, and I don't want the usual shambles. I want the proper distances kept. I want you to look out for snipers, and if any man falls out I'll fine him seven days pay.'

'I'd give him a month's wages if he'd let me off this one,' Innell said.

Karl learnt one thing: the other soldiers in his section might moan and mutter but they were good at their jobs. They could dig their slit trenches in no time while he had to sweat over his.

'Give us the bloody spade, Charlie,' Innell said. 'I can't stand it the way you fart about. Just get stuck in, like this' – and he dug Karl's hole for him. But his idea of discipline was hopeless. He passed muttered comments on every order, and often reduced the NCOs to a state of apoplexy. They got particularly angry because they were scared of him and had to admit to themselves he could get away with anything.

The major went on, 'Any man who drinks water without permission – on a charge. When we get to Rangoon, any man found trying to commit rape – a drumhead court martial; that could result in the death penalty.'

Karl wondered if he was thinking of Innell. 'Certainly not me,' Karl decided, 'in this temperature, with my prickly heat, not a chance!'

They got ready for the march before day-break and trudged through the sand. They saw an Indian soldier stretched out. He had fainted.

'Even the wogs are fainting; they're supposed to like the heat.'

Karl hated the way they always spoke of the Indians as 'wogs' – 'If it wasn't the wogs it would be the Jews,' he thought.

'Thank God they don't know about me.' He could not understand why, but all the men in the Royal Midlands hated the Indians, detested their food, their manners and their way of life.

Innell looked at Karl who felt near fainting. 'Who needs the Japs? We've got our own officers to finish us off. You look crab, Charlie. Come on, give us your pack for a while – ' He went on with a sort of private litany, 'my bleeding feet, my feet are killing me. These bloody wog boots, that's the trouble. Look, me feet are sticking out. Wog made boots.'

He and most of Karl's mates were quite convinced that there was an evil Indian conspiracy to finish them off with inferior equipment. Innell took his boots off, tied the laces together and hung them round his neck. Then he danced a little shuffle dance.

'Oh, I do like to be beside the seaside, I do like to be beside the sea . . .'

'Get back, Innell,' the major shouted. 'Get back. Where do you think you are?'

Innell saluted the major smartly. 'Don't salute, you fool. Snipers!'

Rivers of sweat were pouring down the major like everyone else. The men had been told, 'No saluting. Jap snipers learn to pick out the officers that way.' None of the officers wore their pips, and they had all become curiously keen to carry rifles rather than revolvers. Karl also noted that, Taylor apart, they had become much nicer.

'They just don't want to get shot up the arse. More officers get shot by their own men in action than by the Japs,' Innell hinted darkly.

'Innell, why are you carrying two packs? Give it back to him. Every man carries his own pack. Time he had the Bren. Hand him the Bren.'

Karl began to stagger, then passed out. When he came round, people were talking about him.

'He's flat out, wait till the truck comes.'

'No, I'm all right, I'll get up. I will get up.' But nothing happened. Karl thought, 'They're going to shoot me.' But

154

they didn't; and when he came round properly he was put on a truck. His mates greeted him with hoots of laughter.

'What's the matter then, Charlie, you want to go to sleep with boxing gloves on? It's all right for some, lovely holiday riding on the chara.'

Karl thanked Innell for carrying his pack.

'That's all right, Charlie, you were bloody knackered.'

And now they were going to be let out of the army. Innell said, 'I don't know, the concrete jungle. It's waiting for me!'

Karl was not sure what would happen either. His sister had written, 'Of course we want you to stay with us when you come home. There is a room for you now that Fraulein von Seydlitz has left. It will be good to see you again after all these years.'

When the war in Germany ended she had written, 'I have had a letter from a woman from Theresienstadt. She says she was there when Father died. He did not suffer very much, as he had been ill with enteritis and was very weak. Grandfather, Aunt Cecilia and her old mother are all dead, too. I don't know how they died, but at least we know that Vati was spared one of the worst camps. Theresienstadt was a transit camp, and they deported people from there to be gassed. At least that did not happen to him. I have had news from Aunt Flora, she survived, but not her elder son and his two daughters. I have sent the woman who wrote to us a food parcel.'

Karl felt numb when he received the letter, and did not tell anyone his news. He tried to think about his father and the family but he could not, or would not, grieve. He felt a vast sense of anger against the Germans; how could they allow this to happen? More and more details of the gruesome events that had taken place in Germany during the war were being revealed, and Karl was glad he was not in England, because somehow being in the army in Burma lessened the impact. It was so miserable, so hot, so unbearably humid. The sight of dead bodies was an everyday occurrence, and acted as a protection against grief, an envelope of unreality and suffering that was part of his daily life. 'What about me?' Karl wanted to shout, 'I did not want to be *here*, either.' You had no say at all in where you were sent. His mates had told him what to expect. 'If they give you khaki shorts it's Burma; if they give you those new square respirators it's Normandy.' And shortly after that Karl was issued with tropical gear. Roger, one of his mates shouted, 'I am not, repeat not, going to Burma. I can tell you that. That war has nothing to do with me. I am not going to be killed liberating rubber plantations for some rich swine who means nothing to me.'

Karl groaned with genuine anguish. 'Not Burma, we'll get malaria and the Japs are terrible and I want to rescue my family. Please sergeant, may I have an interview with the company commander?'

The sergeant was irritated, 'What makes you think you are going to Burma? Has the War Office sent you a private telegram? Look here, Hannam, we are not running a holiday camp, you can't just pick and choose where you want to be. So, you speak German. That's very nice, but we are fighting the bastards not talking to them, and the intelligence wallahs – they always know the language. Now stop worrying, fall in outside and stop arguing.'

Karl arrived back in London with a huge kitbag. It was full of tins. He had remembered his brother-in-law's predilection for tins, and on the troopship coming home from India he had bought large tins of fruit salad and Australian pears from the shop. He had also had an attack of fever on the boat, and when he came back from the sickbay found he was so weak he could no longer lift his kit bag. 'I am not lucky with tins,' Karl thought. He remembered an incident in Calcutta. They had been embarking on the ship that was to take them to an island called Ramree in the sea of Bengal. 'It's a military secret where we are going,' Major Taylor had said. 'The enemy is everywhere, must keep our destination secret.'

'Take some oranges to Ramree, sahib?' the fruit seller shouted as they waited to go up the gangplank.

On the quayside there were piles of equipment. Karl spotted some olive painted tins. 'What's in the tins, mate?' he asked.

'Fruit cocktail.'

156

'We are just off on the boat. Can I have a tin?'

'Yeah, here you are, mate.' And Karl stowed the huge tin in his pack, which was already full of ammunition and extra gear of all sorts. He thought it was worth the trouble. How wonderful to eat those delicious little squares of peach, pineapple and pear and drink that sweet syrup. Karl was so pleased he told his mates about it.

'We'll help you carry it, Charlie, we'll have a party when we get there.'

Karl tried to pick his pack up when they got to the island, and he could hardly budge it. He was afraid it would pull him backwards, so that he would be lying on the deck like a turtle with his feet up in the air, unable to move. 'Or what if I fall into the water? I'll sink to the bottom like a stone.'

'Trouble with you is you worry too much, Charlie. Don't worry, it will never happen. Look what they've just given us.' Innell showed Karl two French letters. 'What the hell do they think we can shag in the jungle?' he grumbled. 'Bloody thick things, anyway. Like washing your feet with socks on.' Karl decided he would use his to protect the watch Walter had given him from the tropical damp, and from then on he carried it carefully wrapped in a French letter. He had fainted while carrying the tin of fruit salad, but one day on Ramree they decided to eat it. They told each other 'party tonight' conspiratorially and Karl dug the tin deep into the sand to make sure it would be nice and cool. They were sitting about after supper, waiting for the feast, when Major Taylor came up.

'All comfortable? It won't be long now, a bit of excitement at last. All set for the big show?'

Innell had a special whiny voice he kept for talking to officers. 'Please, sir, can you tell us more about where we are going, sir?'

The major smiled. He liked Innell when he was like that. 'Not yet, Innell, but it's going to be a big show.'

'Thank you, sir.' And when Major Taylor was out of earshot, 'Stuck up git. They want shooting, the lot of them. Come on, Charlie, let's get stuck into the tin.'

Karl had kept an eye on the tin all day, or rather the hole

where it was supposed to cool down. He opened it with the
tin opener on his clasp knife, his mates had brought their
spoons and the tops of their mess tins.

'It's marge, the bloody, sodding tin is full of marge!' he
shouted.

Karl was lugging his kit bag full of tins. He could see his sister
and Walter outside the tube station. They had brought their
car, a huge black thing. They both looked rather brown and
prosperous. Margot was nearly in tears.

'Baby rabbit, baby brother, you are back. Welcome back,
you look so brown and thin. You look so well, just as if you
had been on holiday.'

Some holiday, Karl thought. Oh God, it's started already,
it's still sodding baby brother, but I must not mind.

Walter was more collected. 'Welcome back. I am so glad to
see you all in one piece. Delighted. Come and inspect the
Bentley, it's only a second-hand one but it's very comfortable.
We can't get much petrol at the moment but we thought this
was a special occasion.'

He looked at Karl, 'I am so glad to see you; now it only
seems minutes since we packed you off on that train to Glasgow
– how long was it – four and a half years ago?'

'No, four and three quarters,' Karl thought. 'Where has it
all gone? It's an awfully long chunk of time and I have got
very little to show for it, except that I'm a first class shot, I've
shown qualities of leadership, and got four campaign medals.'

'Karlchen, you look so brown, so sunburnt. You look as if
you have been on a lovely long trip.'

Karl looked at his sister. Was she being funny? He wished
he hadn't sunbathed on the boat coming home, but there had
been little else to do except play chess, and there were not
many people he could play with.

'We have had a terrible winter. Do you know, '47 was the
worst winter for decades. There was so little coal, we nearly
froze to death; even the gas wouldn't work, because there was
always water or ice in the pipes. And the drive was so frozen
up we could not get the Bentley out of the garage.'

Karl was amused. This was suffering indeed. 'Couldn't get the Bentley out of the garage.'

'Well, in India it was so hot I had prickly heat all the time. Your sweat glands get inflamed and you itch all over, but if you scratch the scratches get infected.'

Karl could have added, 'and I had what they called "dhobie's itch" in my crotch, rows of spots that spread outwards in rings; and I got "Bengal rot", too, that comes beween the toes and is treated with potassium permanganate; and then there was scabies, you use purple ointment to cure that. Oh, yes, I was a lovely technicolour picture.'

'We are so pleased you came back here,' Walter said. 'Stay with us until you know what you want to do. We have put something to cheer you up in your room – a bottle of gin, very hard to get but we brought it back from Switzerland.'

'We visited Aunt Hede,' Margot explained, 'but more of all that later. What would you like to do now?'

'Could I have an apple?' The thing Karl had missed more than anything else was apples.

'Of course. And would you like a bath?'

Margot was still looking at him. 'My poor baby brother, how was it? Were they nice to you?'

Karl had no idea how to answer questions like that. He tried to remember how he had felt.

'Were they nice to me?' he thought. 'No, not very, but I was strangely happy sometimes.' At other times a strangling feeling of disgust overcame him; his friends' hatred of the Indians, the misery and futility of the war, being ill. These were the things he could have tried to explain, but all he managed to say, in a voice that sounded to him very unnatural, was, 'Nice isn't quite the word; gradually I'll tell you all my stories. What's been happening here?'

Margot was eager to tell. 'As you know, the Frauelein left, muttering imprecations. She had the strange delusion that she was going to be the lady of the house. I am sure Walter never did anything to encourage that; I mean look at her – and her age!'

Karl was not so sure. He had watched Walter's superb

159

manipulation of her; he also thought that the Frauelein's age was more approximate to Walter's than Margot's. But he reflected, 'For the few months I am going to stay here . . .' So all he did was to ask, 'How is Hannah?'

Margot obviously had not lived in entire accord with Hannah. 'Oh her, well she is amazing. Did you know she trained as a secretarial assistant and now works in the City. I never thought she would have the stamina to last out the course, but she did, and is working now. She has the strangest delusion. She thinks the Frauelein was her best friend, her protector, and *we* have driven her out; we are selfish and unfair and ungrateful. Neither Walter nor I can do anything right. And now she has a boyfriend. As Walter always said, she is a slut, just like her mother.'

Karl wondered if having a boyfriend automatically made someone a slut, and why Margot was so hard on her.

Margot obviously had strong feelings against Hannah.

'Do you know, Karl,' she went on, 'she has no decent standards. At breakfast the other day she put the milk bottle on the table. That was too much for me, and for the first time I said something.'

Karl remembered picking congealed scrambled egg out of a little tin with his clasp knife, sitting with his legs dangling into a small trench they had dug; then again, standing in the jungle with two mess tins, one had tea in it and the other tinned stew, and, balanced on top, the greatest delicacy of all, quite freshly made bread. Then suddenly it had rained, and the rain turned bread and stew into a soggy pulp. Karl had slobbered the lot down because he was hungry. Everything considered, a milk bottle on the table did not seem quite the outrage his sister considered it to be. He had forgotten the passions and concerns of the Levi household, but now it all came back with a vengeance.

His sister, however, was cheerful. 'Tonight we've got a treat for you. We have been invited to the Freunds' for dinner. You may not remember Ilse, but she's a very good friend of mine. She is married now. Walter knew her husband in Berlin, didn't you, darling?'

'Oh yes, very rich; needed to be, he was so ugly, with a *ponim* (face) like that you need to be rich. Well, Ilse is a beauty. You wait till this evening, then you'll see what I mean. Do you still like dark women?'

Dark women? Karl wondered. He could hear the sergeant, when they landed in India. 'Dark – you won't even notice; in three months they all look like bloody Snow White. Watch it, though, don't want you catching a packet, so don't get caught going out of bounds.' Walter, no doubt, was thinking of Gladys. Karl had met her just before he went to India. He had been in a canteen and he was trying to read a book of T. S. Eliot's poems. Not that he had made much headway; he had fallen asleep as soon as he opened the book, and the man sitting next to him snatched it away.

'Hey, what's this, then? A book. I bet it's a horny book. Come on, let's have a look. I like a good horny book. You never know with these clever buggers – always seem to know where to get the best books.'

As the man was in his platoon and much bigger than he was, Karl decided to play it as if it were all a good joke. 'Come on, give it back, you're too young for a book like that.'

But the man would not give the book back. He had it high over his head, inviting Karl either to chase him or start a fight. Either way it would be entertaining.

The land army girl sitting behind them snatched the book and gave it back to Karl. 'You're an ignorant sod, snatching books out of people's hands,' she shouted at the startled soldier. 'You're ignorant, that's what you are, ignorant!'

'What's up with you, Gladys? Do you fancy him? Going for the intellectuals now, are we? Come on outside for a quick one.'

He blew her a kiss, and she said, 'Oh fuck off, I don't go for cheap thrills.'

She climbed over the table and sat down next to Karl. 'What's your name?' she asked him. 'You aren't like the other morons here.'

Bob, Karl's mate at that time – 'your mate is everything,'

the sergeant had told them, 'he protects you, he shares your food, he is like your bleeding wife, you might as well get married' – Bob shouted at Gladys, 'He's a scholar, going to Cambridge after the war.'

Karl wished Bob would not shout his peculiar educational good fortune across the room, and explained to Gladys that he *might* go to Cambridge after the war.

'I was a hotel receptionist,' Gladys explained, 'and then they called me up. Anything's better than factories, I thought, and now I am in the open all right, trimming trees for pit props. It's boring but they say it's healthy.'

Bob yelled across the room, 'Watch it, Charlie, she fancies you. Watch it, you might catch a packet.'

Gladys was furious. 'The only packet *you* will ever catch is up your arse, you nasty little ponce.'

Everyone roared with laughter, except Bob, who went a bit pink.

'That's it, Glad, you tell him.' Someone shouted, 'Stupid twat, no right to say that about anyone. Watch it, Bob, you're going to get a thick ear one of these days.'

Karl could not understand why Bob, who was usually very civil, should be so nasty. But Walter was right, Gladys was beautiful and she was dark, with thick black hair and huge eyes. He remembered the rest of that evening.

'Come on, Karl,' Gladys said, 'walk home with me?'

Karl was frightened. He heard again the warnings he had been given. 'If a tart's after you, watch out! She's likely up the spout already. You know what we do at home? If a tart tries that trick we gets five or six blokes to say they have been through her. You don't know who the father is, then, do you? And the authorities say, "Sorry girl, can't tell who the father is. Too many have been there." You've got to box clever in this man's army.'

As they walked off to her digs, Karl could hear the shouts. 'Get in, knob, it's your birthday.' And Bob singing shrilly, 'I didn't want to do it, I didn't want to do it, you made me love you so.'

When Karl had been staying with the Levis during the leave

162

before he went abroad Walter had offered, 'Why don't you bring your Gladys here for tea?'

It was an idea. Karl and Gladys had nowhere to go in London. 'We can't go to my home, my mum's there all the time. She wouldn't like it if I brought my friends home.' Gladys complained.

But at the front door, outside Walter's house, she had become nervous. 'I can't go in there, it's too posh!'

Karl tried to be reassuring. 'It's all right, it's not really posh. Anyhow it's not my home, I only come here because I haven't anywhere else to go.'

Gladys was miserable and awkward. She said, 'Pleased to meet you,' and after tea stood up and brushed the crumbs from her skirt into the fireplace. Karl could sense the amusement.

'Your girlfriend is beautiful, but this is all . . . well a bit much for her. Isn't it? Never mind, though; if she's "obliging". As my wicked brother would have said, "It's good for your health, any port in a storm." ' And with heavy, hinting politeness Walter excused himself. 'I have things to do upstairs.'

Gladys whispered, 'Come on, make love to me.'

Karl was anxious, 'What if they come in.'

But it wasn't only that, it was the discomfort, the room, the house, the buttons, the fear. Why could he not trust her? Karl could feel the laughter and the sneering. Gladys became brisk and businesslike, 'All right, then, I don't care. I've got to go.'

There were a few letters in which she told Karl 'to keep his pecker up' and 'to take care', but it was never right again, and it all just petered out.

Walter had been respectfully appreciative. 'I think your girlfriend is very beautiful, so natural.'

Karl sensed that 'natural' meant a lack of what Walter considered to be good manners, but he also admired Karl's good taste. As Margot had said, 'Walter likes your girlfriend.'

All that had been so long ago. Since then, the nearest Karl had come to a sexual adventure was in the camp in Bengal; the jungle training camp where he had met Innell for the first time.

Someone struck a shellcase with a piece of metal, it was time for a meal. Karl stumbled through the half-dark camp, clutching his mug and his mess tin. He was not sure where he was meant to be but at least he was in a queue and it wasn't a long one. The men in front were laughing and jostling, and one of them asked, 'Come for a quick one, have you?'

Karl had no idea what he meant until he got almost to the top of the queue and saw the man ahead of him on the ground with his trousers down, wriggling like mad. A small Indian stood by, giving change to the man behind. There was a foetid, fishy smell. Karl's throat contracted and he felt like retching. He excused himself politely. 'Sorry, I think I am in the wrong queue,' and rushed off, thinking, 'A queue for fucking not a fucking queue.' What a place.

He told Innell about it, and he roared with laughter.

'Yeh, this wog comes along in the evening and brings his bibby (woman); you can have her for a chip. That little wog in charge, I goes over to him one day and says, "give", and he hands over all the money. And then he goes to the regimental police, says I robbed him. They put me on a fizzer. "Behaviour prejudicial to good order and discipline", they said.'

Innell was full of stories about his exploits, and when he got going everyone listened spellbound.

'I was going out with this bint in Birmingham, husband was away in the navy. We had a night out . . .' Everyone in the tent gave an anguished howl; they were reminded of the months and years of deprivation.

'Then there was this posh bloke, comes up to me one day, talked all posh like you, Charlie' – Karl felt uncomfortable. They were always on at him for talking posh. Still it was better than a German accent – 'I was only a young squaddie then and this bloke he says, "Can I kiss you," and I says, "No, you bloody can't." I wasn't having that so I got set to put one on him. But he started to cry and gave me his wallet. Dirty bugger. I knew what he wanted, all right.'

Karl thought, 'Yes, I had good friends, not very choice, but they were good friends – and now it's dinner with the posh Freunds.' Walter was still talking about them. His descriptions always included what people did, what money they had, what they had done before the war. Then there was usually a delicious piece of malicious gossip that had Karl chortling for the rest of the evening. The Freunds, it appeared, made ties, very profitably. 'Oh yes, lots of money,' Walter was saying. 'I knew them in Berlin. They were, shall we say, just a little 'nouveau riche'? You must have a look at their paintings, Karl; all chickens. Chickens! Old Freund only bought a painting if it had chickens on it. I have heard of specialization, but this beats everything. Nudes I can understand, but chickens! "Levi," he said to me, "there are two places for animals in this world; on a painting or fried on the plate." '

Margot broke into the conversation. 'You are lucky that they have asked us to dinner. They want to meet you and the food is superb. Do you know the last time we went there we had fillet steak. It was beautifully cooked and in decent slices. You must remember that we are still lucky to get a few pieces of corned beef or a couple of chops a week.'

Walter had been impressed too. 'I asked him, "Where on earth do you get such meat?" and he just looked very mysterious and said, "Well, one has to eat; one has got to have some decent food sometimes." I don't think the marriage is working out well. She seems bad-tempered and irritable. She introduced him to me that day by saying, "Meet my chusband". Do you get the joke, Karl? *Chaser*, that's Hebrew for pig, and husband combined, chusband – not very nice, is it? She is a bit prickly, a bit sharp, it makes me wonder. Fillet steak is all right and so is money, but there are other things. Well, I wonder.'

When they were just about to leave for the Freunds, Margot looked at Karl, 'Do you have to wear that awful uniform?'

Karl was furious. In the first place he had no other clothes except the suit they had given him when he was demobilized. Quite a good suit. But he liked wearing his uniform. It was made of specially good cloth. He had bribed the colour sergeant at the supply stores before they left India. 'How about a decent uniform made of that Canadian cloth?' 'I don't know about that, not many left, none your size, anyhow.'

'Twenty chips?'

'I'll have a look see what I can do, seeing that you are a sergeant,' and he came back with a relatively smart battledress uniform. And now his sister called it 'awful'. Karl was cross and hurt. He knew he could not compete with the extremely well dressed Walter.

'You've got all those coupons. Walter can take you to a tailor on Monday.'

'But I don't want suits like a business gent.'

So he was already cross when they arrived at the Freunds' house because he felt at a disadvantage. There were chicken paintings everywhere. Karl looked at Walter and nearly burst out laughing. He also noticed that Ilse introduced her husband as 'chusband' and that *he* did not seem to mind. He was a big man, plump rather than fat and he was nice and pink. He had powdered his face after shaving and he smelt of after-shave lotion. Karl's Aunt Eunice had sent him after-shave lotion from America when he was in India. The parcel had candy in it which the white ants had got to, but he put the lotion on after his shower and there was nearly a riot. Innell had shouted,

'Come on, then, Charlie, over here. You smell lovely. Come on lad, pick up that bit of soap.' So he didn't dare use it again.

Karl was introduced to old man Freund. His grandmother would have said of him 'he looks as if he has been peeled out of an egg'. His clothes were beautiful, there was not a speck of dust on him and he had a huge diamond stuck into the middle of his tie. 'Just a bit too big,' thought Karl. He shook hands correctly, bowing stiffly from the waist, in the old German manner.

'Ah,' said the old man, 'Back from the wars. What was it like?' But he asked in such a way that Karl knew a reply was not really expected. He felt like saying, 'In Madras I stepped over corpses in the street. They left them there, lying on the pavement, and when they did carry them away they tied them to a piece of bamboo. It jogged up and down as the coolies ran along with it, a merry little jog.' Instead he said, 'Well, I survived.'

'That's good, what was the food like, did they feed you properly?' And Ilse cried sympathetically, 'You poor boy, and

I expect they made you march all the time and carry those heavy bits and pieces. I was talking to the Fish boy, do you know them, a lovely boy, he went to a public school; ah, I will say one thing, they teach them beautiful manners there.'

Karl wondered what he had done already that suggested that he had not gone to the best of schools. He was looking at the table. Margot and Walter had been right, the food was going to be magnificent. Bowls of cut glass were filled to the brim with herring salad, made slightly pink with beetroot; there was tongue on diced jelly, and stuffed tomatoes.

Ilse went on, 'The Fish boy, he went into the army and did very well; he became an officer, and was a captain by the time he was demobilized.'

Margot joined in, 'Well, our Karlchen only got as far as sergeant.'

Walter spoke up for Karl. 'He is wise. I learnt in 1918 that being an officer was not all a bed of roses. They tore the epaulets off officers' shoulders in the streets. I was very happy to be an acting lance corporal – or whatever was the equivalent of that rank in Germany. I always said, keep out of the way and you will survive. I gave you that advice, Karl, you took notice and that is why you are here now, *Prost*!'

But it was not true; Karl had wanted to be an officer. There had been a time when he was thought to be 'officer material'. He had been so keen to do well, had always blancoed his equipment with care when the others could not be bothered. One day the company commander came up to him.

'You seem to be better educated than most of the men here and you give the impression of being keen on the army. I intend to put you forward as a potential officer.'

Karl had glowed with pride. At last his military talents were going to be recognized. The marshal's baton at the bottom of his pack was real. He would look splendid in leather belt, hat and smart gloves. No more trouble with girls, either. He had noticed that they did not seem very interested in a mere private, but surely a subaltern? He had hardly ever spoken to an officer. They stood languidly at the back of the company, if they wanted anything done they gave their orders through an NCO. They gave lectures, too, on 'why we are at war' and 'the history of the regiment'. Karl passed through a number of regiments, and each time he was told that this was the finest, the bravest and probably the oldest. 'Remember,' they said, 'remember Waterloo or Talavera, or Minden, or Mons.'

Karl was called before the regimental selection board. Old Bulletproof, the colonel, was in the chair. He had been shot up by a machine gun in the First War, and seemed to lean to one side. He had a vast number of ribbons on his chest, and although he was very greyhaired, his dark eyes glowed at Karl, powerful with bad temper.

Karl had taken great trouble over his appearance. His corporal had said, 'I don't know why the hell you want to be an officer, but if you do, make them think you are dead keen. All for the Regiment, love the army and dying to have a go. They lap up that sort of bullshit.'

Karl stood to attention before the colonel and saluted so smartly that his arm made a cracking sound.

'At ease, Hannam.' Karl thought that 'at ease' was not quite the right phrase considering how tense he felt, but he banged his legs apart, stamping the ground as he did so, and folded his hands together behind his back.

'I want you to tell the Board how you came to be here.'

Karl felt he had to make it all sound like a happy adventure that had ended all for the best.

'Sir, I came to this country in May 1939. I went to school here . . .' He thought it wisest to leave out the bit about being dumped in an approved school, together with delinquent boys, to become a farm labourer. Far better, at this point, to sound as if he had always led the life of a gentleman.

'I passed my School Certificate, and then my Higher Certificate last year and I have been offered a place at the University of Cambridge. I then volunteered for the army.'

'What games?'

'Sir, I am not very good at games, but I ran for my school and I box.'

'Yes, it says here you are quite a promising boxer. Would you like to join the regimental team?'

Karl thought 'lightning will strike me', but he said, 'Yes, sir, I would like to very much.'

'Why do you want to become an officer?'

'Sir, I don't want to seem immodest' – Karl thought he had achieved a masterstroke of British understatement – 'But I want to do my best in the army and I think I could be of use as an infantry officer.'

He thought to himself. 'What the hell am I getting into? This is a fifth-rate regiment with phony traditions. I want to help with the war to the best of my ability but I am no bloody good at all this and I hate all the bullying and shouting that goes on. What I really would like is to have a nice girlfriend and spend my time in bed with her. I feel lonely and frustrated, sir.' However, Bulletproof seemed satisfied with Karl's manly answers so far.

'Right, Hannam, I'll tell you what we'll do. We will make you a lance corporal, acting unpaid, of course. We will see how you get on and if it turns out that you can cope we will send you to an officer selection board.'

Karl saluted smartly and was led out. The next day his promotion was duly announced and he wore his tape. Bob asked him sourly, 'Still speaking to me, corporal? I'll have to watch my step now.'

Karl realized that this was exactly like the time when he had been made a prefect; only this time he was expected to shout and bully.

Another corporal advised him. 'Trouble with you, Charlie, you're too much of gentleman. You don't ask the sods. "If you please, will you do something?" You threaten them and they must know you mean it.'

Karl thought grimly that just when he had succeeded in internalizing the values of Elmfield, and had learnt to carry the burden of authority with reason, understanding and gentleness, all this had to happen. Now he had to bully.

'Come on,' he shouted, 'make a pukkah job of the beds.'

'Get stuffed,' one of the men snarled at Karl. He was an older man and not impressed with this youthful lance corporal.

'Don't put a man on a charge,' Karl had been warned, 'they

won't back you up. They'll just say you lack the qualities of leadership needed. The men should follow you naturally.'

'Who the hell do you think you are, telling me what to do?' The man, an ex-artillery gunner disgruntled at being converted into an infantryman, shouted at Karl. Karl started to say, 'Shut up. Everyone will hear you,' but the abuse continued.

'I am not taking any orders from a bleeding, acting, bleeding unpaid, bleeding lance corporal.'

It was even worse with the senior warrant officer. 'What's this, then? Our aspiring officer. Wants to be a gentleman, does it? A student in civvy street, oh ai say, posh were we? Well laddie, you're not an officer yet, not by a long chalk.'

It went on for weeks and Karl was miserable. His own mates had been posted, no one took much notice of him and the new soldiers realized very soon that he had no real authority. 'I lack the qualities of a genuine officer and gentleman,' Karl said to himself, and he felt dispirited when he was called for another interview with Bulletproof. A major did the talking this time. The old man sat at the side and looked as if he was half asleep.

'Now, corporal, tell us what you have been doing?'

'Sir, for the past four weeks I have been acting as a lance corporal.'

Old Bulletproof awoke from his stupor. 'What do you mean acting *as*? You *are* a lance corporal. It's the most important rank in the army and you talk as if it did not matter. Dismissed.'

Sergeant Major Binks marched Karl out of the presence. For the first time he spoke to him almost kindly, 'Made a right balls of that, didn't you?'

So Karl just contented himself with saying that he had not been very interested in taking His Majesty's Commission. He kept to himself that he had hated the boredom, the petty bickering, the crudity, the lack of privacy. And how he continually had to do things he hated doing, like climbing high ropes. The chusband said that he had wanted to join but, sadly, his asthma was too bad.

Ilse retorted sharply, 'You wouldn't have survived for a

170

fortnight.' And Karl thought that it was a miracle *he* had.

By now the conversation had turned to the past. 'It's St Bernard time,' Karl thought. He was thinking of the hoary refugee joke: the dachshund claimed that at home he had been a St Bernard. Walter was enjoying himself and was telling about the time in Berlin when he had helped the British Consul.

'He was a charming man, of the old school, you know. We played tennis together once a week. One evening he said to me, "I wonder if you can help me with a small problem; it's the Polish Jews. They all want to go to Palestine, and our rule is that before we give a visa they must produce a thousand marks to prove that they will not be destitute when they get there. We have a limited quota for entry permits, but if they have the means of support we must give a visa. Now I know that they show us the money and then pass it on to the next man. They are circumventing the regulations." I said to him "I can help you with that one. Why ask to see cash? Ask them for evidence from their bank manager that they have that amount." I can tell you, he was impressed with such a simple solution. He said, "Mr Levi, thank you. If you ever want help . . ." and of course we did a few months later, and he was very helpful.'

Everyone nodded approvingly, but Karl was appalled. Walter, civilized, humorous and kindly Walter, had clearly been responsible for dozens of Polish Jews not getting their visas. What was worse, no one seemed to mind that they had probably perished because they could not get out. Karl felt physically sick and went to the lavatory. He could not keep down such people's food, even though it had been his favourite herring salad and golden fried chicken with cucumber salad. He put his finger down his throat.

'What's the matter?' his sister asked sympathetically. 'Have you been sick? Your eyes look all red.'

Karl said, 'I am sorry, I've had stomach trouble ever since my jaundice in Burma.'

Ilse was sympathetic. 'You should see our Doctor Kahn. He is good with upset stomachs and things. Shall I make you some tea?'

171

When they were back in the Levi house, Walter asked, 'What did I tell you? Wasn't the food good? And what about the happy couple? I could sense irritation and frustration. What gruesome furniture. You could use each piece as a lethal instrument. "Gelsenkirchner baroque" I would call it. Well, tomorrow I'll show you the factory.'

Chapter 9

'We have stopped making the floor polish,' Walter said. 'When the war ended we knew the big boys would be bound to start making real polish again, so we got out while the going was good.'

He smiled happily. 'Never mind, we didn't do too badly. And now it's dolls – pink dolls, brown dolls, dolls with sleepy eyes, dolls with mama voices, and guess what else? Toys for budgies! We have this genius, he comes up with ideas, and one day he said, "Plastics. That's the new thing." So we moulded plastics. Little balls, big balls. And suddenly we thought, put the little ball on the big ball and you have a tumble toy. Put a tiny ball on a small ball and you have a toy for budgies – what's more, it's going well. Let's stop here. I walk the rest. Don't want to upset everyone by rolling up at the front door in a big car.'

Karl was amused by the nimble business mind that had been displayed before him. He had never been inside a factory before, and while what Walter said made good sense, the reality of the factory horrified him. It was a huge, decrepit shed, windows broken, filthy, and with the mixers making a dreadful din. They walked through several lines of workers who took no notice of them, and climbed up to a dingy office. Walter sounded unusually hearty.

'Karl, I want you to meet Mr Kirsch. Mr Kirsch, Karl Hartland, my wife's brother, just back from the wars.'

Karl sighed. He had resigned himself, to the fact that none of his relatives had accepted his new name.

Mr Kirsch positively cringed with pleasure, 'I am so pleased to meet you, particularly one of Mr Levi's family. Coming to join us? It's a good business and we are just beginning to grow into a major concern, aren't we, Mr Levi?'

Kirsch seemed to need Walter's support for most of his statements. When he said 'Are you going to join us?' Karl could almost read his thoughts: 'Levi's bringing in the family and I am going to be thrown out.' Karl wanted to reassure Kirsch and tell him that he would sooner shovel wet shit than work here, but he did not have time to get a word in edgeways. Kirsch looked at him. He was clearly keen to please Karl as well as Walter.

'Ah yes, in uniform. Very smart, too; and all those ribbons. What are they for?'

Karl was pleased that at last someone had asked him about the ribbons on his chest. His sister hadn't seemed at all interested. He wanted to sound modestly heroic so he put an undertone of restrained pride into his voice.

'Well, this is the 39/45 star, and that's the Burma Star. This one is the Defence Medal, and the last one is the Victory Medal. Everyone got that one.'

It was not as straightforward as Karl made it seem. He had fallen ill when they had been in Burma for only a few weeks. It was just after they had left Ramree Island and were on their way to Rangoon for 'the big show', as Major Taylor had called it. And not only the major. A very, very senior officer covered in red tabs had come.

'Attention, Battalion Royal Midlands,' the colonel had shouted.

Innell was near Karl, who heard him mutter, 'Stupid bastard, petrol feet. Do you know his batman told me he has straw in his pack so that he looks like the lads but doesn't make his back sore. The git, couldn't organize a piss-up in a brewery.'

The very senior officer stepped forward and told the men to gather round, so that they could feel the occasion was important but not too formal.

'I am proud to be able to tell you that at last you will be

174

able to have a crack at the Jap. I know you have been waiting eagerly, and now is your chance to be in at the kill. You will join a combined operation. We will hit the Jap and we will hit him hard.'

The colonel bawled, 'Royal Midlands, three cheers for the general.'

Karl heard a loud 'boo' from his side. He did not dare to look. The sergeant scanned the ranks desperately and the major hissed. 'If I catch anyone in my company booing I'll have him court martialled.'

There *was* a cheer, three cheers in the end, but it was a very thin effort and Karl thought it was mainly from the officers.

Karl felt ill and dispirited. When they were sitting in the landing craft going up the river to Rangoon he heard Innell singing. 'I don't want to be a soldier, I don't want to go to war,' and thought 'and I don't want my bollocks shot away.' He remembered the tale he had heard in the training camp where they had been 'prepared' for the jungle. 'There was this kid, and the Japs caught him and they screwed him, the whole sodding battalion, all of them went through him. Found him afterwards, he were sobbing his fucking heart out. The colonel said, "Never mind, lad, we'll get them for you. We'll pay them back for that," and he went for the Japs with a sword and a whistle. Mad bastard.'

They had been trained for the landing. 'When that ramp goes down I want you out there like shit out of a goose. Straight out, or they'll shoot you before you've even seen the bleeding town.'

Karl had been told: rifle at the alert, safety catch off when you land, and move, move. His back ached and he had told Innell that his pee was dark brown. Innell had laughed.

'Dark brown? You've caught a packet, welcome to the club.'

Karl protested.

'Of course, you don't do things like that, do you, Charlie? It's the heat, boy. Dries you out and your piss is like boiling acid.'

175

Karl sensed the contempt in 'you don't do things like that'. He had considered trying but the little pimp had folded back the girl's labia, when she was lying on the ground.

'Look sahib, saf hai (it's clean), schoolgirl, no illness, clean jig-jig.'

It was the smell, the look on the girl's face. Karl stuffed a rupee in the man's hand and ran off. Perhaps he had caught it off his hand.

'Don't come to me,' the medical officer always said, 'telling me you got it off the lavatory seat. Funny place to take a woman, that's what I say.'

The marine who was in charge of the craft shouted. 'Right, ready to land, ramp down, out!'

Karl rushed out, all tense, his rifle at the ready. This, he felt, was his moment. This was what they had sweated and trained for. Karl looked round, trying to be sharp and alert. A small Burmese boy came up to him. He held an egg between thumb and forefinger.

'Buy an egg, sahib?'

Major Taylor screeched with disappointment.

'They've gone! The Japs have gone. We'll march into the town.' He looked at Innell. 'I'll have any man caught looting, or anything else, shot. Understand?'

'Look at those tits, those lovely Burmese tits!' Innell moaned as they tramped through the town.

They put up for the night in a large European house. They were told it had been a Japanese officers' mess. Karl went upstairs. There was a smell of rotting rice, but in a shattered bathroom he came across a pair of socks and a tube of toothpaste on a shelf. The tube had Japanese writing on it. He picked it up and the dreadful thought came to him, 'How could I kill a man who cleans his teeth? A man who reads magazines and who leaves socks behind because he runs away and is scared?'

In the night Innell came back. 'Here you are, Charlie. We found a bank. We're bloody rich, man. Look at this.'

He had wads of Japanese occupation money in his hand. Karl remembered the major 'any man caught looting . . .' but he could not refuse Innell.

176

'Hey, Charlie, and you know what, we've found a brothel. It's lovely, and they'll let us have a jump for a tin of sardines. Curly's been. They're mad on sodding sardines, do anything for a tin. Come on, Charlie, I'll show you.'

'Sorry, I can't. I'm not interested. It's my back. It aches.'

'Why don't you report sick? Anyroad, give us your tin, then, if you don't want it.'

The medical officer looked at Karl the next morning.

'Yes, you have got jaundice, all right. Beautiful yellow. We'll have you evacuated in no time.'

He wrote 'infective hepatitis/malaria?' on a white label. Karl was pleased, more than pleased; but a bit of him wanted to stay. He did not want to let on that he was scared, hated the sight of bombed out warehouses and beggars, and the smell of corpses and rotten rice.

The doctor said, 'No, we don't take any chances with jaundice. Can't be treated here. We'll have you on the hospital ship in no time.'

When he was back with the battalion after weeks of hospital and sick leave the war was over. The atom bombs had been dropped over Hiroshima and Nagasaki and the rest of his platoon were applying for their campaign stars. Karl wrote Chota's application for him.

'You do it, Charlie. I'm not so good at writing.'

So Karl wrote: 'Sir, I respectfully submit this my application . . .'

He read through the regulations. They stated quite clearly that anyone who had been evacuated with honourable sickness (that meant not VD, they decided) was entitled to the 39/45 star even if he had not been in Burma for the required six months. Karl thought he might be one of the few in the battalion entitled to the star. All the others were not going to get it because they had only been in Burma five months. So he wrote out a letter for himself as well. Within a few hours he was called before Major Taylor, who sat there with just the Burma Star on his chest. Anyone who had been on the other side of the Brahmaputra river could have the Burma Star, and there was not much distinction in it. The major held Karl's application up as if he had just fished it out of a full lavatory bowl.

'Private Hannam, what's this application? The 39/45 Star? Nonsense, you were sick. You can't have the star.'

Karl thought, 'I'm not afraid of you any more, you hysterical piece of shit. Anyhow, you can't stop me.'

He stood smartly to attention. 'Sir, it *is* the regulation. If you would care to read it you will see that I'm right.'

'You were sick, you were evacuated with some illness. If *you* can get the star any Tom, Dick or Harry who caught a packet in Rangoon can have it.'

'No, sir, only if it is a legitimate illness. There is no entitlement if it was venereal disease.'

Karl remembered that Innell had told him, Taylor had caught syphilis in Calcutta. 'Perhaps he's suffering from dementia praecox,' he thought.

'Sir, if you think I can't have the star, may I have an interview with the colonel?'

Major Taylor was really cross now. He knew he could not refuse, and if Karl went to the colonel it would look as if he had been unreasonable.

'You, Hannam, are a barrack-room lawyer. You always argue the toss and you think you are very clever.'

Karl thought, 'Cleverer than you, but that's not much of an achievement.'

'I have noticed you are writing other people's letters of application for them. I tell you what I think. You are one of those reds trying to stir up trouble. It's ridiculous. People got killed to get that star and you get it because of some piddling regulation. It makes me sick.'

Karl thought. 'No. What makes you sick, mate, is that you haven't got it and you are a regular. You need the fruit salad on your chest so that you can get on.'

Karl really wanted the star just as badly as Taylor, and the best thing was that he was going to get it and Taylor wasn't; that really made it worthwhile. The only thing to be said in favour of Major Taylor was that he was equally unpleasant to everyone. Karl annoyed him in a particular way, but Private

178

Innell annoyed him even more, however, and he knew some gossip about the major.

'Do you know, Charlie,' he said, 'what that bastard did in civvy street? Sold ladies' underwear! Think of it! Pink knickers. I bet that was a thrill for him, the poxed up old git.'

Karl could not really tell Kirsch all about his medals and so he just said in a deprecating voice, 'I suppose they will be useful when I'm selling newspapers on the corner.'

'Oh Mr Hartland, or what is your name now, Hannam? You won't have to sell newspapers. Join us here. We are in a growth industry, aren't we, Mr Levi?'

He looked up to Walter as if for comfort and assurance and then he bustled off.

'Must check the supplies. It has been a pleasure to meet you. Perhaps I will see you at coffee time.'

As soon as he was out of the room Walter said in his confidential, slightly pitying voice. 'What a *nebbich,* that Kirsch. He is our accountant. I think he even keeps an account of exactly what he has produced when he goes to the lavatory. Freud, I believe, would describe him as the perfect anal type – just what you need to be a good accountant. He is very dependent on us. I am sure no one else would put up with his cringing and creeping. But if you think he is odd, you should meet his wife. She is one of your classical hysterical types – and we know what is lacking to produce that type, don't we? Now they live beneath a Miss Samuels in a Hampstead flat and Miss Samuels is a good fourteen stone. Every time she moves, everything in the Kirsch flat rattles. They write the poor lady angry letters every day. I said, "Look, why don't you swap flats? If Miss Samuels was below, then you wouldn't have any complaints." But they won't do that either. I think they are scared they will be lost if they have nothing to grumble about. They might even have to look at each other. And they've no children. As we used to say in Berlin, "Children's shit is the best glue to hold a marriage together." '

Karl thought, 'it didn't help you much, did it? And I wish you would stop coming out with facile Freudian interpre-

179

tations of everything. Ben got over that one in the sixth form.'

Walter's old schoolfriend, Borod, came in. Walter had already given Karl an introductory talk about him in the car.

'Borod was in the gunners in the First War. He is the strongest man I have ever known. He used to heave shells about as if they were milk bottles. Look at his hands and his shoulders; he really is tough and just the man we need here. There is a place for someone really tough with the sort of workpeople we are forced to employ. Nowadays we have to take whoever comes along. Mind you, sometimes we're lucky. You will see Vicky, a real beauty,' Walter cupped his hands over his chest.

'She is special, a beauty. But that fool Borod has taken her on. I said to him, "Borod, don't be an idiot. When her husband comes out of jail you will get carved up." Borod takes no notice and gives her silk stockings and things. Mind you, when you meet his wife you will understand why he goes on like that. What a tart, what a bitch. She has always hated me. She resents our friendship and the fact that her husband has to work for me. She has a "special relationship" with Felsenberg; do you know him, the art dealer? Last Christmas we were having a drink at Borod's house and there was a charming little Florentine primitive on the wall. I went up to it and asked where it came from and Borod said innocently, "Oh, Felsenberg is lending it to us. He hasn't got enough room at the gallery." Ho, ho, I thought, more likely for services rendered. The cow must have guessed what I was thinking because she was looking daggers at me. I just wondered if she was worth such a nice picture. No doubt she is good at it, she's experienced enough. But still, a Florentine primitive . . .'

Borod said, 'Well, young Hartland – what is it now? Hannam? I don't know all these new names.'

Margot had already commented, 'Are you going to change back to the old name? It's a fine old name. There is nothing to be ashamed of. I can't understand why you stick to that weird new one, which no one can spell.'

Borod went on, 'What do you think of it here? Better than soldiering? What next? Studying? What use is that? That won't make you any money, young man.'

He rushed out and a few moments later came back in carrying a sack full of clay. To him it seemed no heavier than a bag of sugar.

'Careful, Borod,' Walter warned, 'you will rupture yourself, and with *your* spare-time occupations that won't be very helpful. You need all your strength at the moment.'

Borod roared with laughter. 'That's all right, there's plenty to spare. Well, Mr Soldier, how about you? God, when I was your age I was screwing myself silly; even spent my pocket money on it. It all went to the local madam, didn't it, Walter?'

Karl remembered Vanessa's beautifully modulated and precise voice, saying, 'The price for good girls is whores. When women are exploited, and they certainly are in this age, the upper classes send their young men to the brothels so that the virtue of their own women can be preserved. Economic pressures drive working class girls into the brothels. Do you call this double standard civilized, or the basis for an adult, dignified relationship? Men have made women inferior and exploit their economic dependence, and don't tell me that giving women the vote has made much difference.'

Borod asked Karl, 'How would you like to work for us?' He turned to Walter, 'He could take the samples to Leicester, we have just lost our man there. Let's see if you can sell our marvellous dolls. Look.'

He showed Karl one of the dolls – and it was a poor thing. The seam along the middle had not been filed off and Karl thought a small child might well tear its hands on it. The clothes were badly made and the eyes, that were supposed to move, stayed half-open.

Borod said, 'It's a good doll for the poorer sort of customer. It doesn't cost too much and you could carry it with the budgie toys. Let's see what you can do.'

Karl was in conflict. He had to do something. It was nearly a year before he could go to Cambridge and he could not possibly just sit around all that time. The thought of selling something intrigued him; perhaps he would be a good salesman. He could be making money and discovering a new talent at the same time. So he agreed to go to Leicester. Kirsch gave him a list and a brown suitcase. When Karl picked the case up it made a soft meowing sort of noise.

'It's the mama-dolls,' Kirsch explained. 'Now. You take a cheap day excursion ticket; you can easily do the firms on the list. We pay your expenses, but don't lunch in the Ritz. Good luck!'

Karl planned the operation by setting out the addresses so that he could visit the shops nearest to each other. He put on his new demob suit. It was dark blue herring-bone tweed, and no worse than the suit he had worn at school. The ridges on the shoulders indicated mass production and the buttonholes were certainly not hand-finished like the ones on Walter's suit. They had given him a hat when he went through the demobilization centre and he put that at the bottom of the case. Really he still felt most at ease in his uniform, but had to admit that it was not the right kind of dress for selling toys.

The first shopkeeper was not very encouraging. 'Sorry, mate, we have done our ordering for Christmas.'

'But Christmas is months away. Wouldn't you like to look?'

'Not interested.'

The next shop owner looked at Karl. 'Just demobbed, eh? I can spot one of those suits a mile off. Come back from the wars, eh? Well, let's have a look.'

The suitcase was unpacked; he looked at the dolls. 'Finish not very good, is it? Eyes don't open properly, do they?'

Karl was torn between loyalty to the firm and his own honesty, but he agreed that the finish was rather poor and added, lamely, 'That's why they are so cheap.'

'Cheap be buggered. They're not! No thanks, sorry.'

It went on like this from shop to shop. Karl felt depressed. He was sure Kirsch had chosen the shops specially because he knew Karl would find it hard to sell anything to the owners. He said to himself, 'One more. And if that's no good. I'll go back to London and they can stuff their flaming dolls.'

The shop to be given the last chance was a large one. Karl's instructions said he was to ask for Mr Bush. He turned out to be a large and unpleasant looking man, who leered at Karl.

'What do you want? Do you mind, I am busy with a customer.'

Customers are obviously more important than salesmen, but it occurred to Karl that shopkeepers had to spend so much time being civil to customers they vented their spleen on salesmen. Mr Bush returned in a foul temper. 'What's this, then? Dolls? We have got all the dolls we need.'

But nevertheless he made Karl unpack the case and held up a negro doll whose eyes remained firmly shut even when he shook her. Karl said, 'She's meant to be a sleeping doll.'

'Don't try to be funny with me, young man.' Mr Bush retorted. 'We have to sell them, you know. Why waste my time coming here with inferior goods. If you want to see proper dolls come and have a look at these.' He showed Karl a row of glamorous, fair-haired well-made dolls. 'Tell whoever your boss is not to send me rubbish like that again,' he said, as he showed Karl the door.

Karl decided that was the end of his career as a salesman and took the next train home. At the factory they did not seem all that surprised, and Karl wondered how they kept going. Walter said, 'Well, there *was* a toy shortage, but perhaps it is coming to an end. We do very nicely in some parts, though. Never mind, you're just not right for this kind of thing. It's no use being scrupulous; shopkeepers have to be encouraged to buy.' He said, 'encouraged' in such a way that Karl realized he meant 'bribes'. He was cross that no one had told him that. It looked as if they had wanted him to fail.

Karl scanned *The Times*. A preparatory school wanted a young man to teach general subjects, live in and help in the boarding house. Karl felt quite excited. This was for him; he could live in the school, and then at the end of the year move on to his Cambridge college. No further struggles with his conscience and reluctant buyers. He wondered what his qualifications for teaching were. He had a place at Cambridge, but what did he know? He vaguely remembered the content of the letter of grievances Luther had pinned on the door of Wittenberg Cathedral; he could name quite a few of the Renaissance popes; and geography? Was he not well travelled? He remembered the 'lesson' given when they approached India. It had come through the tannoy system on the boat when they could just see Bombay, and certainly smell it.

'You are now approaching India,' the posh voice droned 'the crown of the British Empire. You are here to protect India from the invader. We are fighting together with our Indian comrades in the great Indian Army. It is teamwork that will win us this war and it is your duty to respect the greatness of this nation.'

The man squatting next to Karl spat. 'Dirty wogs. All they eat is curry. Stinking bastards. I hate them.'

When Karl landed he was given a topee. The sergeant said, 'The sponge inside is to be kept wet, to stop you getting heat-stroke. Keep out of the sun, it's dangerous. Any man suffering from heatstroke will be charged with having inflicted an injury on himself. Be careful with the water. You have been given anti-mosquito ointment and this will be put on before sunset. It is a punishable offence to neglect malaria precautions. If an area is marked "out-of-bounds", keep out, or you will be in danger of being attacked by hostile mobs incited either by communists or by Congress wallahs. *And*, if you are caught going into a brothel or if you catch VD you will be charged.'

Karl thought, 'Welcome to the Empire!' as the sergeant went on, 'Watch out for the beggars and the loose wallahs. They'll steal anything, but especially your rifles. I knew a man who had his arm cut off because they wanted his rifle. Sleep with your legs wrapped round it at night.'

'What will they cut off then?' Karl wondered with dread.

'The loose wallahs, they're the worst, shave off their hair and cover themselves with grease so you can't catch them. They are so clever they can take your wallet from under your pillow at night.'

What an unpleasant country they seemed to be protecting from the evil Japanese invader! What, Karl wondered, had become of the great Hindu and Muslim civilizations.

'Watch out for the Congress wallahs, they are the wogs who want us out of the country. They love the Japs; would have them in the country in no time. The educated wogs, they are the

184

worst . . .' ('I suppose they might say that of me, too. I am supposed to be educated, aren't I?') '. . . they think because they have been to some wog university they can run the country, but they can't, they're useless. Watch out. Once they start tucking their shirts in, that's when you want to be careful. They think they are better than us.'

'Shove off, you black bastards,' his mates snarled at the beggars. When they were on the train someone threw a tin of jam out of the window. It hit a beggar on the head. 'There you are, you black bastard, there's some connor (food) for you. The only decent ones are the char-wallahs,' the can-thrower went on. 'They come from the North-West Frontier. They sell us char and wads, and with the money they save they buy rifles. Then they shoot at us on the Frontier.'

They were told, 'If you kick a wog, kick him up the arse. Their religion won't allow them to show their arses so they can't complain. Then there's the Hindu untouchables. If their shadow falls on the food of someone in a higher caste, he has to throw it away – and they're bloody starving most of the time. Ignorant, that's what they are.'

Karl remembered the endless train journeys. He really ought to be able to teach geography.

He marvelled at the confidence of his fellow soldiers. They were so completely convinced of their superiority in every way. Their food was better, their manners more civilized and their moral standards not open to question.

'Ignorant, that's what they are. Worship the cow. I ask you, worship a shitty cow. The cow can do what it wants here. If you run over one they'll tear you apart, but if you run over one of their chicos fifty chips will do the trick. You get anything for money here – 'ere, chico, idderow (come here) gooblewallah? twelve annas?' and they would roar with laughter and so would the child, timidly, because with British soldiers you never knew what to expect; one moment sweets and chat and the next an angry kick up the arse.

The colonel had said, 'If you catch a loose wallah there is only one thing I ask of you. Don't leave the corpse outside my daftar (office)' – roars of laughter.

Yes, Karl thought, he was definitely entitled to teach geography; and physical training. After all his splendid marches and his boxing, surely he would be able to help form the characters of little boys at a preparatory school.

Soon after his return from Burma, his sister had asked him, 'Do you remember Mr Charc?'

Karl's reaction to questions of this kind was usually guarded. Whenever his sister said, 'Do you remember . . .?' she would follow it with, 'Well, he's dead.' The Germans had been so thorough, that most members of the family he remembered were dead. The exceptions were Aunt Flora and one of her sons, another aunt in Switzerland and his father's partner Mr Mond and his wife. Now there was news of Mr Charc. When Karl was still a boy in Germany, Mr Charc had taught him how to box. He ran a gymnasium with a special appeal to Jewish families. They hoped that a course in physical training would make their young tough and lean, and possibly acceptable to the National Socialists. Karl had loved going to Mr Charc, who never teased him about being fat or clumsy. On the contrary, he had discovered in Karl a potential weight-lifting and boxing champion. Margot had good news of him.

'I had a letter from him. He has survived the war. He was called up and became a corporal in the German army; he even survived Russia. It's a rather pathetic letter. He obviously has not got much left now and I sent him a food parcel with some tins and a small quantity of coffee; that's worth its weight in gold in Germany at the moment. And some cigarettes. He was a very decent man.'

Thanks to Mr Charc Karl had ended up in the regimental boxing team. He quite liked the training – skipping and hitting a kitbag full of sand. But then came the regimental boxing match. Old Bulletproof was there, slouched in his special chair, with the other officers near him sitting upright. Karl did not know until the last minute whom he was going to fight then, to his horror, found it was to be 'Smudger' Smith. Smudger was notorious. He was continually going absent without leave, and had got into real trouble one day when he hit a corporal and was put in the regimental prison for fourteen days. During that time he had been set to digging flowerbeds and doing packdrill with a heavy pack on his back. He was truly fighting fit. Moreover, he hated non-commissioned officers even more than real ones.

Smudger might have been the same weight as Karl but it was distributed differently. His shoulders were wide and his hips slim. He was tattooed all over. Karl was fascinated by the men's tattoos. One had 'death before dishonour' with a dagger on the forearm; others wore gravestones with 'mother' on them; or jokey tattoos like, 'cut along the dotted line', and 'never full'. Smudger's tattoos were artistic. He had a lion on each shoulder, and laurel leaves and flags across the chest ending up with a central bunch of British flags.

Karl's mates were there to watch his bout. They had, for the time he was in the ring, forgiven him for joining the enemy and becoming a lance corporal.

'What horrible luck,' Curly said. 'Not Smudger! He's a wild sod.' But Karl hoped perhaps it would turn out all right; after all, he had never done the man any harm.

'It's not your fault,' Curly explained, 'but you are an NCO. He hates NCO's!'

And now Karl stood in the ring, facing Smudger in the opposite corner, with his arms on the ropes, steadying himself. Some of his mates were shouting, 'Come on, Charlie' which was nice of them; but Karl was wondering what would happen if he just lay down and refused to fight. On balance he decided he would get worse treatment, so he stood and waited.

The bell went and Smudger hit Karl very hard. Karl wanted to shout, 'That hurt. Come on, this is not a serious fight, take it easy.' But Smudger hit him again. Then Karl got in a blow and made Smudger's mouth bleed, but he was hit again. As he went down he saw the lions on Smudger's shoulder very clearly. He tasted blood and snot in his mouth. He forced himself up and tried to fight but was not able to do anything very effective. After that the bell went. Someone sponged his face and said, 'Keep on at him, you're doing well.'

'Sod it,' thought Karl, 'if that's doing well . . .' and then the bell went again.

After three rounds, during which Karl went down several times, Smudger was declared the winner. They shook hands and the next two contestants were ushered into the ring.

Curly said, 'What did you keep on getting up for? You're stupid, I would have stayed on the mat the first time. What made you keep on? Bloody stupid this boxing. You know what it is? Blood sport for the officers. Makes them all randy to see us bashing each other over the head.'

One of the officers stopped Karl later. His head was aching, he had several bumps on his face and every time he moved his neck it hurt.

'Well done, corporal, that was a good clean fight. You kept going, that's the main thing. Well done.'

Karl said, 'Thank you, sir,' and thought that at least some one appreciated him. But he was more pleased when, later, Curly was inclined to be complimentary.

'It pays to be handy with your mits in the army. I bet you will have less cheek now when you give orders. Now they know you can put them on their backs they'll be more careful.'

Karl had a letter from the preparatory school. It was called Sodenham, was a recognized establishment and the headmaster was an FRGS. Karl checked the school in the yearbook, and was relieved to find it actually existed. He found out that FRGS meant Fellow of the Royal Geographical Society, and that anyone could become a member on payment of a five guinea fee. However, he thought, who was he to quibble about that with no letters after his name at all and nothing but army experience to offer. The letter also said that the vacancy had occurred rather suddenly and the newly appointed man was to start straight away. Karl went for the interview. The house was at the end of a half mile walk along a drive lined with rhododendrons. The building looked Elizabethan from a distance, but when Karl got closer he could see that it was very recent Elizabethan – parts of the roof were covered with corrugated iron.

'So you have come for the post?' said the secretary, a four-square, very Scottish lady who, Karl thought, must have inspired Tenniel to draw the Red Duchess in Alice. 'Have you had a good journey?'

Yes, Karl had had a good journey and he also thought the weather was mild for the time of the year.

'I'll take you to see the Master now.' She knocked, and bent down slightly to listen for the imperious, 'Come'. The Master was a very pink gentleman wearing a clerical grey suit. His pinkness was that of a man who had not been in the open air for years. He had white hair and his mouth drooped. It was very clear that he was in charge.

'Ah, Mr Hannam, you want to come and work here?'

'Yes, indeed.'

'And what subjects can you offer?'

Karl thought he would teach anything from needlework to football to get the job, but confined himself to general subjects.

'Actually, sir, I am going to read History at Corpus.'

'Good, a historian. Can you turn your hand to a bit of English too, and games?'

Karl, hoping again that lightning would not strike him, said, yes, he would be pleased to help with games.

'Where did you go to school?'

'Elmfield.'

'Where?' He sounded impatient.

'Elmfield, sir, in Sussex.'

'Where are you from?'

'A good question,' thought Karl. He had prepared himself for that one and said, 'I grew up in Sussex, sir.'

It seemed to satisfy. Karl felt a vast sense of relief. At last the continuous, 'and where are you from', was going to stop. He had passed over, he was about to be an Englishman, teaching at a proper school. The Master spoke generally about the close connections the school had with adjacent public schools, the quality of the pupils, and his great desire to keep them happy. Suddenly he seemed bored with the interview.

'I can offer you £45 a term, and, of course, you will live in. You may have noticed the gatekeeper's cottage at the bottom of the drive. The young men on the staff share that. I would like you to start straight away. I was let down by the man I appointed and we are a member of staff short. Can you come at once?'

Karl said he would be delighted, but did the Master not want to see any references? He wanted to produce his demob book, on which it said that his behaviour had been exemplary. He could also have asked Steve to say something about him. But the Master dismissed the suggestion with a regal wave. 'I hope you will be happy with us. This is a happy school and we all work very hard.'

Karl said he looked forward to joining the staff next week, and left. On the train back he was well pleased with himself.

'I have got a job as a teacher in what looks like a very distinguished school. They seem to think I am English and find me acceptable; *and* I have got somewhere to live until term begins next October.'

He told Walter and his sister what he was planning to do. Walter said, 'Yes, well, if that is what you want to do. Can I now tell you our plans? But this is in strictest confidence . . .'

Everything is always 'in confidence' Karl thought crossly. The same 'secret' is peddled round to all, but no one knows for sure if anyone else knows, so all the time you have to watch what you say in conversation.

'We are thinking of going to the States,' Walter went on. 'As you know my mother has already gone. My sister insisted that she should go there at the earliest possible opportunity after the war ended. I think she rushed her too much, though. She flew as soon as a seat could be found for her on a plane.'

Margot laughed. 'The first thing that happened was that she got a poison ivy rash from a bunch of flowers that was put on her bed to welcome her. Here is an old lady, protected from ever having to face up to any sort of real life and what happens – she gets a poison ivy rash!'

Walter did not find Margot's amusement at his mother's misfortune all that funny. He went on, 'Now we are thinking of going, but I haven't discussed it with the children yet. Of course, Fred is still in the army but he will be out soon, and Hannah has led her own life here – that is another reason I

190

want to take her away. We wondered if you would like to come with us? There are excellent opportunities over there, and I really think this country is on its knees. They have exhausted themselves in the war. The fuel crisis last winter was the last straw; if a country can't even keep warm, it's the end.'

Karl disagreed, but kept his thoughts to himself; 'I don't think this country is finished at all. An interesting social experiment is going on, because the Labour government is really trying to eradicate inequality. So fuel was short last winter. Tut tut. I don't think that is sufficient reason for clearing out.'

He asked Walter what he was planning to work at when he got to America.

'I am not sure yet, but I have got good connections in New York. Someone here is trying to buy me out of the factory and I think this is a good time to move on. We would like you to come. I am sure all the family in the States would welcome you and I expect they would be pleased to send you to university there. I believe you could help towards paying your fees by working as well.'

'That's just it,' thought Karl, 'I don't want to be surrounded by family. I don't want to be paid for by anybody, I don't want to owe anything to anybody, I have had enough of dependence.' But all he said was, 'I think I want to take up my place at Cambridge. It seems such a good opportunity and my fees and everything will be paid by a government grant. I won't have to ask anyone for more money.'

Walter sounded a bit hurt. 'Please Karl, don't think that anyone would mind helping you along, and you would be quite independent. I can understand that at your age you would want to be on your own.'

For a moment Karl was tempted, being with a family had its compensations, especially the comfort. But he so hated the tensions, the bickering, the emotional pressure and the manipulation. 'Perhaps I have learnt to do without a family,' he decided, and answered as tactfully as he could.

'I think I want to stay here, at least for the time being – until I have finished at Cambridge. I'm not sure what I want to do and if I go and teach now I'll find out if I like it.'

Margot was not exactly cross, but she felt that there was a certain lack of loyalty in Karl; first he had dropped the family name and now he was going to let them go to America and live in England on his own.

'Well, baby brother, I expect you know what is best for you,' she said, and that was that.

Chapter 10

Karl had a week to spare before starting at the school and decided to go and see his Aunt Flora and have a look at his home town, Essen. He had received the money due to him after demobilization and his gratuity. Furthermore, when she left England Margot had handed him a cheque for more than a hundred pounds. 'I sold some of the things I brought with me from Germany,' she said, 'things like the dinner service, some silver and linen. We can't take everything with us to the States and I thought you should have some money in case of emergencies.'

Karl was pleased and might have been grateful had she not found it necessary to add, 'It's for emergencies, mind, and not just frivolous amusement.'

Karl thought, 'After all the years I have spent living riotously in the army! Who does she think I am or what have I been doing?'

Again and again Karl was deeply annoyed by how little anyone understood what had been happening to him. His family were always either moaning about the dreadful winter and how lucky he was to have missed it, or discussing where you could get decent chickens. Another favourite topic was who was making what and how much, and, having made it, where they would choose to go for their holidays so as to get round all the currency restrictions. In the event, all he said to Margot was, 'Thank you very much, very useful. I am going to Brussels to see Flora and then I shall try to get into Germany.'

Aunt Flora's flat was in a very expensive block. As he stepped out of the lift Karl recognized the scent. It was the same he had known in her house in Germany, a mixture of a special sort of beeswax and clean linen. A warm, homely smell. He rang the doorbell and a pale, apologetic looking lady opened the door.

'Ah, you must be the famous nephew. Good morning, Herr Hartland. May I introduce myself? I am Frau Krohn and I look after your dear aunt.' She walked ahead of Karl and announced him at the entrance to the drawing room.

'Here he is, he has arrived, your Karl. Doesn't he just look like his dear mother?'

Aunt Flora was much smaller than Karl, square, and almost bald. Her remaining strands of hair were laid across her skull, but only emphasized the empty space; certainly did not hide it. She was wearing a black dress and a black shawl. Karl was nearly in tears, he wanted to throw his arms round her and hug her but she stepped back, held her hand out and said very firmly, 'Well, good day, here you are at last. I hope you are really hungry, we have a good lunch waiting for us.'

She was keeping to the formalities to hide deep emotion, that was obvious. Karl could see that her eyes were damp, but she went on undeterred, 'Let me introduce Frau Krohn. She looks after me wonderfully. I don't know what I would do without her.'

Frau Krohn seemed deeply pleased. She reminded Karl of Walter's mother's companion. There was the same admiration, flattery and submission.

'It's nice of you to say so, but really you don't need me.' She turned to Karl, 'I am just a luxury, here in case something unexpected happens. She is so independent. I'll get the lunch ready,' and she went out into the kitchen.

Aunt Flora said by way of an explanation, 'She spent two years in Bergen Belsen,' in rather the same way that in England one might have said 'Winchester and Oxford'. It was as if that explained everything about Frau Krohn.

Aunt Flora looked at Karl and smiled. 'You have become a giant. Last time we met was your barmitzwah, wasn't it? You were smaller than me. Now look at you. You're a young giant.

And you were a very fat little boy. Do you know, to me you are the spit-image of your dear mother. Oh, what a lot has happened since then! So much! The scoundrels, the scoundrels!'

She said 'scoundrels' with deep feeling. It was the worst word Karl ever heard her use about those who had murdered her and Karl's families; but it was a good word. It conveyed what she felt all right.

'You must wonder, Karl, how it is that I am here at all. Well, it's a long story, and it's hard to believe that it's all true. Anyhow, you remember your uncle Julius' – Of course Karl remembered Julius. His favourite uncle. The one who had stuck a needle into his eye when he was an apprentice, the one who had told him he did not believe in religion any more, not since his little boy had died. The uncle who had been unable to resist fingering the lapels of your suit and muttering, 'that's a nice piece of cloth – Worsted?' For the first time in years Karl found he was thinking of his uncle Julius. But Flora was still talking.

'When the war was about to break out, Julius and I fled to France. Our two sons had already gone, Kurt to Belgium and Gerd to Argentina – but that's another story. Do you remember Kurt had two daughters? Irma and Frieda? We used to joke about you and the daughters. We thought you ought to marry one of them. All that Hartland money and the cloth factory put together, a very interesting proposition. But now that's all in the past, all gone. Oh, the scoundrels. When the Germans invaded France Julius and I were interned by the French. The camp commander, a very charming and civilized man said, "You must flee before the Germans come or it will go badly for you." It was all too much for your poor uncle Julius, his heart just gave up. He died very peacefully and I have often thought he was the luckiest of us all. He was a wonderful man, you know, a real man, strong and gentle. No one will ever know what he meant to me. We packed up our few belongings and fled. My younger son, Kurt, they caught him and he ended up in Belsen. He survived and the British freed him but he was too weak. He was so starved and feeble, he could not hold on to life; he just died. I talked to Mr Bergmann, he was a partner of ours, a nice man and very decent. They were together right through Belsen until the last moment, and do you know he told me that the day before Kurt died he was planning for the future. "Bergmann," he said, "when this mess is over we will open a new branch in Amsterdam. Let's expand." And the girls, Irma and Frieda, well, they went off so cheerfully. They were laughing and joking and we gave them what money we could. They put it in special belts round their waists. The plan was that they should go to Switzerland, where they would have been safe. We never heard of them again and we have no idea what happened to them.'

Flora gave a muffled sob. 'That picture over there, that's Irma. They gave us that bronze for our silver wedding anniversary. Do you know, right through the war a German officer and his family lived in this flat. They must have been decent people, because everything was in tip-top order when I came back. I talked to Gerd about the girls and I said to him, "Do you know what I fear most? It's that the girls were abused sexually, that the Germans let the soldiers use them." They are gone, everything is gone. Oh, the scoundrels.'

She paused for a moment, then her voice became calmer and she went on. 'It's as if it had all been wiped off a blackboard, all gone. After Julius died I wanted to get back to Brussels. I had nowhere else to go, and so I took a train right across France to Belgium. It was full of soldiers, but they took no notice of me. I just sat there, like a little peasant woman going to market, and they did not even ask me for my papers – which was just as well because I did not have any. Julius always used to tease me, said I looked like a Westphalian peasant; well, if I did it saved my life that time. In Brussels, instead of going back to my flat, I went to see Colonel Laplage. He was an old friend, and he said to me, "Madame, do not be afraid, we will protect you." You see, he had married a German girl from Aix-la-Chapelle after the First War. It was a bold thing to do and it cost him dear; he never got any more promotion. And she was not a Jewess either. She was an Aryan. Neither of them had any reason to do what they did for me except that they were friends of mine. They had a little room and they put a wardrobe in front of the door so no one knew it was there, and that is where I lived for the next three years. I used to go out in the evenings, but during the day I stayed there, not daring to make a sound. If the Germans had found me it would have meant certain death for both of them. Do you know, Karl, how I managed to survive? I never told a soul where I was living, not a soul. There were informers everywhere, who got paid if they gave useful information to the Germans, and then there were those who talked if they were arrested. Other refugees I met in the evenings said to me, "Don't be so secretive, for goodness sake. Where do you live?" But I never told anyone. And they all got taken away, one after the other. I remember one man, for example, he was not afraid of anyone or anything. He had been in the Buchenwald camp during the first wave of arrests before the war started. They hit him so hard, they broke his arm, and all he said was, "they can't harm me." He escaped from the Germans and went to Brussels. He walked about everywhere, a huge man, carrying his little dachshund under his arm. He was so conspicuous, the Germans found him in no time after they overran Belgium and he disappeared, poor man. All of them gone, the scoundrels. He thought he had no need to take care, and he paid dearly for it.

'When it was all over, in 1945, we moved back to this flat. I asked my cousin Alice to come with me because I could not stand being alone. But it didn't work. She told me, "I can't stand it." You see, all her family were dead. At least I had one son and his wife, that was something. But she had nothing. One day she screamed, "I can't stand it any longer," and she cut her throat with a carving knife, rushed to this window and threw herself out. I could not stop her, what could I do?'

Flora went limp as she was telling Karl about it. There was no anger in her manner, just desperate sadness. 'The police came. Do you know, Karl, they wondered if I had done it. They said it was unusual for someone to cut her throat *and* jump out of the window. Had we quarrelled, they asked. I suppose they had to do their duty.'

They ate an enormous lunch. 'Come on, Karl, eat up, you

haven't had enough. We got this chicken especially for you. Frau Krohn, give him another piece. We must feed our Englishman properly. You are a proper Englishman now, Karl?'

Karl explained that he was a naturalized British subject and intended to go on living in England. Flora said wistfully, 'It is wonderful to be settled in a country and to belong. Look at my son, Gerd, and his wife, the travels they have been on. They went to the Pyrenees, and they had a bad time there. Food was short and they just could not get their share. Do you know what they did? One of the girls in the breadshop in their village was a bit simple and so they used to walk up and down until she was serving because she would always give them something. Everyone was unpleasant; no one wanted them. My son still says that he can't bear the sight of the gendarmes, they remind him of that time. After all, after the war had begun they could have been handed over to the Germans at any time. In the end they got visas for the Argentine but first they had to get to Portugal and they needed transit visas to get across Spain. But the Spaniards were not prepared to let them through. In the end a friend in Paris got them Portuguese visas. He told my son, "They have no validity, but if the Spaniards know you have permission to go to Portugal, they might let you through." It worked. They got a ship and crossed the Atlantic. Imagine what that was like, U-boats everywhere. When they got to Jamaica, the British interned them. But my son said that was a really nice camp and they were treated well. When they produced their Argentinian visas they were allowed to go on to Cuba and from Cuba to Buenos Aires. Your Uncle Eric was there already to welcome them. Do you know, Karl, you are very like your Uncle Eric.'

'Oh god,' thought Karl. But Flora liked Eric. She did not seem to share Margot's prejudices and thought she had paid him a compliment.

'A beautiful man. He got a bit too fat towards the end of his life, but he was a good and loyal man – oh, Karl, what times we have lived through. The scoundrels.'

From Brussels Karl went on to Essen. He wanted to see the town, perhaps to exorcise the painful memories and also, somehow, to confirm that these places had really existed. The town was still in an incredible state – not just in ruins – it looked as if the actual ruins had been bombed. The streets had been cleared – the rubble simply bulldozed aside – and the trams were running again. The people looked grey and shabby and Karl had never seen such destruction. The first thing that struck him was the smell. It was rancid, foul, and the same everywhere.

Later Herr Mond explained, 'There is hardly any soap; what there is, is made of sand and clay. It's a miracle there is not more disease.' About the bombed town he said, 'Do you know, there have been discussions as to whether the whole ruin should not just be left where it is and a new start made somewhere else. But in the end it has been decided to rebuild, at least the foundations and sewers are still here.'

Herr Mond and his family were not Jews, but they had stayed loyal and devoted to the bank and Karl's father. They had done what they could, but had to stand helplessly by when Karl's father and the remainder of the family were taken away. Karl had arranged to go and see the Monds because he hoped he would get some clue, some understanding, of what his father had been like and what had happened after he had left. He had brought presents for the Monds: a tin of instant coffee, soap, and cigarettes. Frau Mond fondled the soap.

'You have no idea what a pleasure it is to smell real soap again.'

She had cried when she had met Karl for the first time. 'Oh Karl, you are a fully grown man now. It has been so many years, and what years.'

Herr Mond had been a huge fat man when Karl had left Germany. He still had his large frame, but under his chin the skin hung down in loose folds; there was a wide space round his collar and all his clothes hung on him as if they had been made for someone else. He handed Karl a small package.

'They're rings. Your father asked me to keep them for you and your sister and I am glad I can give them to you now. They belonged to your grandmother and your father was really worried that you might never get them. Come on, let's have

199

a cup of coffee somewhere, or at least what they call coffee these days.'

Karl pocketed the package with the rings in it. Herr Mond was despondent, 'What a time we have been through, and it is not really much better now. What a mess this country is in. First those criminals got us into the mess, and now they have gone. What will become of us? No one can do anything until the currency is re-valued, and I am not even sure that will work, either. We are ruined.'

Frau Mond was crying, 'We saw your father just before they took him away. He was so ashamed, because after you left he had to wear a big yellow star on his coat and he could not bear it. He hated being conspicuous and never wanted to go out. We used to take them food, but in the end there was nothing for them. It was dreadful. The worst time was when the Nazis were winning. Every day there were radio announcements, church bells ringing and jubilation all round. I said to myself, "It will never end. They will go on for ever." If I wanted to weep I had to go into the woods. If anyone caught you looking sad they suspected that you were not delighted with the victories.'

Her sobs increased. 'The dreadful crimes that were committed. How can I ever again be proud of being German? I used to pray, "Please God, make it end." '

Herr Mond was very uncomfortable. He could not bear the open display of emotion. He was moved by his wife's misery, but wanted her to hold it in so he said rather gruffly, 'Oh come on, Inge, Karl is here and we want to enjoy the day. Stop crying. Let's be thankful that we are still alive. Look, I have got a treat for us.'

He produced some slices of very unmeaty, pink-looking sausage. 'I got these at the butcher's round the corner, no ration points either. I am a big eater, and really being so short of food is difficult. But I won't complain. We have survived the war and we are together. Our boy was not even called up into the Volksturm. They tried to, but he is going to be a mining engineer and that got him an exemption. It may seem ironic to you, but he was a lot safer down the mines than anywhere else. I always said, if we can't give him a fortune when we go, at least he will have learnt a useful profession. There is work for mining engineers all over the world.'

Karl wanted to know what had happened during the bombing. Frau Mond said, 'We had this little house, a hut rather than a house, really, in the Harz mountains. We were safe there until the last days, when there was some fighting nearby and the roof was blown off. We did not know what to do but then some Italians came along and although we were terrified at first, and thought they would cut all our throats, they explained that one of them was a carpenter and they would mend the roof for us. In return we gave them shoes, because they only had rags on their feet.'

Karl found his way to the house he had lived in until he left Germany. He rode there by tram. It was a fifteen minute ride but only one or two stops before he arrived did he begin to see some reasonably intact houses. He was just about able to find his way. Everything seemed to be smaller than he remembered. Even the distances were shorter. He reached the house. It had been bombed. The bomb had fallen in the front garden, and the whole house had slipped forward. Karl looked up, right into his parents' bedroom; the yellow wallpaper was still there and some large pieces were flapping loosely in the wind. The bottom windows had been bricked up. The trees were all still there and the willow still had some pieces of black fungus growing on it. When he was a little boy, Karl remembered, his father had said, 'We must do something about the willow, it needs to be treated and pruned.'

The garden at the back was wild. The trees on the verandah had got so thick they had grown right into the metal frame. The place was desolate and deserted. Karl felt he was intruding. There was nothing for him there any more. The house where he had lived such a long time ago was no longer a real part of him. He felt numb and sad. He knew now that his childhood had ended.

Karl reported to the secretary at Sodenham.

'Ah, there you are. Had a good journey? Don't you think it's rather chilly for this time of the year? Several of the boys have got colds already. I will tell the Master you're here and then I'll introduce you to your colleagues. I am sure you'll get on well with them. Mr Gravell is just out of the forces and he starts at Cambridge next year, too. You should have a lot in common.'

The Master did not seem very pleased to see Karl. 'Hmph, so you have come. Well, there's a lot to do; get unpacked and we will give you a time-table. You don't mind taking a bit of biology, do you?'

Karl did not mind at all, but he was worried about the Master's lack of enthusiasm at his arrival. At the interview there had been moments of charm, and even a little interest in him as a person, but now his existence was hardly acknowledged. Karl was shown his room in the cottage. It was painted cream and the furniture was a bit sparse. There had been a wood fire in the grate, but it had burned out. A tall man rushed in. He wore a tweed coat with leather patches, had a droopy military moustache and a pasty, spotty complexion.

'Ah, good, you must be the new man. Glad to see you. I am fed up with taking all the games. Just out of the forces? Where were you?'

Karl explained that he had been in Burma and had just come back from India. 'My name is Charles,' he added, hoping to be friendly.

'Gravell, John Gravell, I am just back from the Palestine Police.'

'The Palestine Police!' Karl screeched inwardly. There had been nothing but depressing news from Palestine. Karl had been sickened by the way the British government was treating the refugees from the continent. The *Struma,* a boat full of them, had been sunk by a mine after it had been refused permission to dock in Haifa. Karl was appalled by the thought that people who had survived the horrors of the concentration camps were not allowed to live where they wanted after all their suffering. From all accounts, the Palestine Police were trying to keep out Jews, were anti-semitic and pro-Arab. That at least was the view of the *New Statesman,* which Karl read every week. He hoped that Gravell would not, perhaps, be like that. After all

202

he'd only been a conscript and was possibly no more in favour of what was going on than Karl had been among soldiers who despised and hated everything Indian. But he decided to be very guarded, and Gravell soon proved that his caution was justified.

'Yes, the Palestine Police. I was invalided out. The strain, those blasted Yids, they tried to blow us up, terrorist bastards. I know what I would have done if I'd had my way. So you're going up next year, as well? Corpus? Well done, I am going to Selwyn.'

Karl nearly said, 'Oh bad luck,' but restrained himself in time. 'What's it like here?'

'All right. The kids need keeping down, insolent little swine. I had a whole class in tears today. I'll teach them to play about while I am talking. I warned them; and now they know the sort of chap they're up against.'

Gravell's chin went up and he looked bellicose and tense, the red spots showing up even more.

'Oh Lord, the fire's gone out; it never stays alight. They're too mean to give us coal, just wood, and then only what they chop down in the grounds. Did you know that we are in forty acres of woodland?'

Karl's second young colleague came in. He had cheap, hornrimmed glasses on, a school blazer and a poor looking shirt. His shiny school tie was held in place by a brass pin. He looked like an aged caricature of a schoolboy in a magazine. He sniffed and unwound a college scarf.

'The fire's gone out. Did you let the fire go out?'

This was obviously a long-standing grievance between him and Gravell.

'No, I didn't let it go out, it went out by itself. I was taking the Colts for practice, wasn't I?' Gravell turned to Karl, 'Footer or Rugger?'

Karl would have liked to say 'neither', but thought it wiser to say 'both'. He asked what had happened to his predecessor. George rubbed his hands to get warm.

'Not sure, just left, didn't seem to fit in.'

By implication, he fitted in all right and assumed that Karl would. Karl noticed his sniff. Every forty seconds or so he sniffed nervously, and at the same time swallowed a ball of spit which made its way noisily down his throat. Gravell might be anti-semitic, but at least he didn't sniff. The interrogation continued.

'Where have you come from? Where do you live?'

Karl's answers were sketchy. He had already made up his mind that he would not tell actual lies but would leave certain areas very vague. So he 'was brought up in Sussex', and lived with some of his family in London; that was as much as he would say. If pressed further he would look tragic and indicate that he did not like to talk about certain sad things. This approach worked well enough.

'So you were in the Army?' George went on. 'You're lucky (sniff), they wouldn't have me; health reasons. How did you get here? Truman and Knightly, or Gabbitas?'

Karl said he had seen the advertisement in *The Times*.

'You're lucky. If you use the agencies they pocket seven-and-a-half per cent of your first year's salary. They don't pay you here until the end of the term, by the way. It's blue murder, everything on tick from the village shop.'

Karl offered him a cigarette and they both took one. Gravell said, 'You've still got duty free, lucky swine, I'm right out. I've got to smoke to keep calm. Let me show you something.' He rushed out and came back with a black cap with a shiny badge. 'There, I've still got my cap. I wanted to join the Guards but then this opportunity came along, and it seemed a good way to see the world. Were you on internal security as well? Good stuff. Smash the wogs, agitators, trouble makers!'

He kicked the logs into the fire as if they were a sort of substitute for some poor Indian. Karl tried to turn the talk away from India and find out about the school. 'What sort of duties do we have?'

George answered. 'There's a lot to do. You are on from eight till eight, and if you make any mistake you get shot. You've got to get it right.'

Gravell joined in. 'First thing in the morning you have to ask the little beasts if they've "been", and if they haven't they go to matron for dosing. Yes, they keep you busy all right. Must be off now, English and then prep. For once try to keep the fire going. I had dozens of boys bring wood here. It was supposed to go to the old man but I re-routed the traffic. One thing about the Service, eh, Charles, you learn the dodges.'

Karl offered George another cigarette which he took greedily.

'Ta, haven't had a smoke for ages. I'm a bit short right now, old man. You couldn't lend me half-a-dollar, could you; until the end of the week, that is?'

Karl was suspicious and said he was a bit short himself. Everything about George inspired mistrust. His elderly school-boy manner, his sniffing and his desperate keenness. He wanted to be Karl's mentor. But Karl said to himself, 'Whenever one is new anywhere the first approaches are always made by the shits and rejects and they have certainly put me among them.' George did not seem particularly offended at having been re-fused a loan. He brought out a box full of numbers. He was cutting out numbers from an old calendar and sticking them on large sheets of paper.

'I am drilling them in tables. If I put these up they'll learn them better. You'll find there isn't much in the way of equip-ment here. They don't give you anything, but I want the Master to know I'm keen. They've got to know you're keen. This is a good place, and I want to stay here (sniff).'

Karl tried to read, but Gravell rushed in and left the door open long enough for the draught to scatter George's numbers all over the place. George was shrill. 'For goodness sake, show some consideration. Now my numbers are all over the place.'

'*Mafish*, bad luck, as they say in Arabic. Who cares? Kids don't take any notice of you, anyhow. How's it going, Burma-wallah?'

Karl groaned inwardly. This was going to be like a phony army mess with snatches of Arabic thrown in as an extra. Gravell was making copies of an examination paper. The copy-ing was done from a clay tablet on which he spread the master sheet which was supposed to leave purple ink on the clay. As he lifted the master sheet, the clay came up as well.

'Oh hell, bloody hell, this is the end!'

He picked up a chair and threw it against the wall. Absurdly the chair got caught between the wall pannelling joints and stuck, hanging high in the air. It was like a surrealist painting.

George was shocked, 'Steady on, old man, you can't go damaging the Master's property.'

'Bugger the Master, bugger this rotten school!'

'Mr Gravell, you're biting the hand that feeds you.'

'Feeds me, the rotten stuff we get. Call that food? Rotten kids who don't want to learn. Those Levenson boys, for instance – bloody four-by-twos!'

Karl was puzzled, and then realized this was rhyming slang. Four-by-two, army equipment, a small piece of flannel for cleaning rifle barrels, rhymes with Jew.

Gravell was in fine flow now. 'I want to kick them in – yids. I tell you, Charles, Hitler had the right idea, should have gassed the lot, then they couldn't have killed my mates. Yes, gassed the lot.'

Karl wanted to say, 'Look here, I am a Jew, you can't say things like that.' But then he felt it was too late. He had concealed his origins, and now he would either have to leave or have it out with Gravell. He felt utterly depressed.

'Is it ever going to stop?' he wondered.